2nd edition

Solutions

Elementary Workbook

Tim Falla   Paul A Davies

OXFORD
UNIVERSITY PRESS

OXFORD
UNIVERSITY PRESS

Great Clarendon Street, Oxford, OX2 6DP, United Kingdom

Oxford University Press is a department of the University of Oxford.
It furthers the University's objective of excellence in research, scholarship,
and education by publishing worldwide. Oxford is a registered trade
mark of Oxford University Press in the UK and in certain other countries

© Oxford University Press 2012

The moral rights of the author have been asserted

First published in 2012

2016 2015 2014 2013

10 9 8 7 6 5 4 3

ISBN: 978 0 19 455326 1   Workbook
ISBN: 978 0 19 455282 0   Audio CD
ISBN: 978 0 19 455281 3   Pack

Printed in China

This book is printed on paper from certified and well-managed sources

ACKNOWLEDGEMENTS

*The authors and publisher are grateful to those who have given permission to reproduce
the following extracts and adaptations of copyright material:* p.60 Extract from *Oxford
Bookworms Library 3E Stage 1 One-way Ticket – Short Stories* by Jennifer Bassett.
© Oxford University Press 2008. Reproduced by permission; p.103 Extract from
Oxford Bookworm Factfiles Stage 1 London, by John Escott © Oxford University
Press 2007. Reproduced by permission; p.104 Extract from *Oxford Bookworms
Library Third Edition Stage 1 A Little Princess* by Frances Hodgson Burnett © Oxford
University Press 2008. Reproduced by permission; p.105 Extract from *Oxford
Bookworms Library: Stage 1: 400 Headwords The Coldest Place on Earth* by Tim Vicary
© Oxford University Press 2008. Reproduced by permission; p.106 Extract
from *Oxford Bookworms Playscripts Stage 1 Five Short Plays* by Martyn Ford
© Oxford University Press 2008. Reproduced by permission; p.107 Extract
from *Oxford Bookworm Factfiles Titanic* by Tim Vicary © Oxford University Press
2009. Reproduced by permission.

The publisher would like to thank the following for permission to reproduce photographs:
Alamy Images pp.48 (Hay bath/Westend61 GmbH), 48 (Ice sauna/isifa Image
Service s.r.o.), 57 (Modern art display/Iain Masterton), 71 (Snow resort/The
Photolibrary Wales), 82 (Factory production line/Jeff Morgan 02), 91 (4x4 desert
driving/Grapheast), 99 (City of London School/imagebroker), 100 (Cafe/Yadid
Levy), 102 (male and female doctor/Gabriel Blaj), 103 (grocers/Neil Holmes),
103 (woman reading a book/Holger Burmeister), 103 (Waitress Serving Food/
Ocean/Corbis), 103 (men in coffee shop/Fancy), 103 (pub/Greg Balfour Evans);
Bridgeman Art Library Ltd p.90 (*Captain Cook taking possession of New South Wales,
1770*, illustration from 'Hutchinson's Story of the British Nation', c.1923 (colour
litho), Gilfillan, John Alexander (1793–1867)/Private Collection/The Stapleton
Collection); Corbis pp.6 (Puppy chewing shoe/Radius Images), 30 (Woman
practising martial arts/image100), 36 (Day of the Dead/Danny Lehman),
54 (Alcatraz Island/moodboard), 63 (Albert Einstein/Bettmann), 64 (Nelson
Mandela/Patrick Durand/Sygma), 66 (Salvador Dali/Bettmann), 72 (Mount
Fuji/Image Plan), 100 (American football/Jeff Lewis); Education Photos
p.29 (Summerhill School/John Walmsley 2011 All rights reserved); Getty
Images pp.4 (Teenagers talking/Michael Krasowitz), 10 (Buckingham Palace
garden party/Tim Graham), 14 (Teen boy with basketball/Denkou Images),
18 (Ballroom dancers Anton Du Beke and Erin Boag/Simone Joyner), 28 (Skiers/
Alexa Miller), 84 (Backpackers/Radius Images), 92 (Walkers in Kings Canyon/
Paul Nevin), 98 (Portrait of teen girl/Nathan Blaney/Photodisc), 101 (world
largest restaurant in Bangkok/Patrick aventurier), 105 (Captain Robert Scott's
Expedition to Antarctica/Popperfoto); iStockphoto p.99 (Red Carpet illustration/
soberve); Kobal Collection p.107 (*Titanic*/20th Century Fox/Paramount/Wallace,
Merie W.); Oxford University Press pp.11 (Young man/Digital Vision),
11 (Businesswoman/Fuse), 12 (Farmer/Cultura), 13 (Teen couple/Fuse), 30 (Judo
match/Score by Aflo), 43 (Students Writing/Frederick Bass), 43 (Teenagers
studying/Image Source), 43 (Students talking/Comstock), 53 (Businessman/
Somos), 53 (Businesswoman/Digital Vision), 54 (Golden Gate Bridge/Digital
Vision), 61 (Man in restaurant/Thinkstock), 61 (Family having Thanksgiving
dinner/Radius Images), 71 (Chimp/Digital Vision), 71 (Tropical beach/Corbis/
Digital Stock), 74 (Brown bear/Photodisc), 74 (Lion/Digital Vision), 74 (Crocodile/
Paul Springett), 76 (Rhino/Ingram), 76 (Panda/Ingram), 97 (Vet/Digital Vision),
97 (Man talking to female doctor/Gareth Boden), 100 (Golden Gate Bridge/
Photodisc), 101 (Machu Picchu/Photodisc); Press Association Images p.48 (Beer
bath/Eret Petr/AP); Rex Features pp.38 (Absolut Ice Bar/Nils Jorgensen), 84 (Woman
teaching in Mozambique/Design Pics Inc.), 98 (*Dancing on Ice*/Ken McKay/ITV).

Cover: Alamy Images (China, Hong Kong, Ma Mo Temple/Achim Sass).

Illustrations by: Humberto Blanco/Sylvie Poggio Artists Agency pp.5, 22, 27 (ex
3), 34, 35 (ex 2), 44 (ex 3), 45, 51, 69, 75, 80, 81, 88, 89, 95; Claude Bordeleau/
Agent 002 p.56; Rob Davis p.106; Paul Daviz pp.19, 27 (ex 2), 33 (ex 5), 35 (ex 5),
37, 47, 55, 77, 85; Glyn Goodwin p.62; Clive Goodyer pp.6, 7, 8, 16, 26, 31 (ex 1),
33, 41, 44 (ex 1, ex 5), 52, 70 (ex 1), 71, 72, 87; Andy Parker pp.20, 31 (ex 2), 46;
Mark Ruffle p.70 (compass); Gwen Tourett p.104; Fred Van Deelen p.102 (map).

UNIT		A	B	C	D	E	F	G
I Introduction	p.4	Meeting people	*be*, possessives and pronouns	*have got* and articles	Time, days and dates			
1 Friends and family	p.8	Family	Present simple: affirmative and negative	Royal party	Present simple: questions	A day in the life	Introducing people	A message
	p.15	**Self Check 1**						
2 My time	p.16	Free-time activities	Adverbs of frequency	It's fun, but is it sport?	*can* and adverbs	Extreme sports	Expressing likes and dislikes	An announcement
	p.23	**Self Check 2**						
Get Ready for your Exam 1	p.24	• Listening • Reading • Use of English • Writing • Speaking						
3 At school	p.26	School subjects	*there is / there are*; *some / any* with plural nouns	Schools without classrooms	*have to*	Karate school	Giving directions	A letter
	p.33	**Self Check 3**						
4 Special occasions	p.34	Clothes	Present continuous	Day of the Dead	Present simple and continuous	Celebrity lookalikes	Making arrangements	An invitation
	p.41	**Self Check 4**						
Get Ready for your Exam 2	p.42	• Reading • Listening • Use of English • Writing • Speaking						
5 Healthy living	p.44	Food	Quantity	Unusual diets	*should / shouldn't*	Feeling good?	In a café	A questionnaire
	p.51	**Self Check 5**						
6 Going places	p.52	In town	Past simple: *be* and *can*	Teen adventure	Past simple affirmative: regular verbs	A postman flies home	Asking for information	A note
	p.59	**Self Check 6**						
Get Ready for your Exam 3	p.60	• Reading • Listening • Use of English • Writing • Speaking						
7 Fame!	p.62	On the map	Past simple affirmative: irregular verbs	Changing the world	Past simple negative and interrogative	Famous artists	Talking about your weekend	An email message
	p.69	**Self Check 7**						
8 In the wild	p.70	Geography	Comparative adjectives	Landmarks	Superlative adjectives	Dangerous!	Negotiating	An advert
	p.77	**Self Check 8**						
Get Ready for your Exam 4	p.78	• Reading • Listening • Use of English • Writing • Speaking						
9 The world of work	p.80	Jobs and work	*going to*	Jobs for teenagers	*will*	A year out	On the phone	An application letter
	p.87	**Self Check 9**						
10 Time to travel	p.88	Transport	Present perfect affirmative	Down under	Present perfect negative and interrogative	Adventure in Australia	Buying a train ticket	A postcard
	p.95	**Self Check 10**						
Get Ready for your Exam 5	p.96	• Listening • Reading • Use of English • Writing • Speaking						

Reviews p.98   **Extra Reading p.103**   **Functions Bank p.108**   **Writing Bank p.110**   **Wordlist p.112**   **Self Check Answers p.119**

I Introduction

IA EVERYDAY ENGLISH Meeting people

I can introduce myself and other people.

1 🎧 **LISTENING 2** Complete the dialogue with the sentences below. Then listen and check.

And how old are you?

G–I–A–C–O–M–O.

And you. Where are you from, Annaliese?

Fine, thanks, Iris. And you?

Hi, Annaliese. How are you?

How do you spell your name?

I'm seventeen too.

Hi, nice to meet you.

I'm seventeen. What about you?

I'm fine too. Annaliese, this is Giacomo. He's from America.

I'm from Australia.

Iris	1	Hi, Annaliese. How are you?
Annaliese	2	Fine, thanks ... And you
Iris	3	I'm fine too. Annaliese this is Giacomo. He's from America
Annaliese	4	Hi, nice to meet you.
Giacomo	5	And you. Where are you from
Annaliese	6	I'm from ...
Giacomo	7	And how old are you?
Annaliese	8	I'm seventeen ...
Giacomo	9	I'm seventeen too
Annaliese	10	How do you spell your name?
Giacomo	11	G–I–A–C–O–M–O

2 🎧 **LISTENING 3** Listen and write the words.

1 name
2 school
3
4 ten
5 pencil
6 house
7
8 desk

3 🎧 **LISTENING 4** Listen and write the numbers.

a 7   d 23   g 16
b 13   e   h 1
c 11   f   i 3

4 Write the numbers as words.

2 two   21 twenty-one   3 three
8   40 forty   19 nineteen
15 fifteen 12 twelve   6 six

5 🎧 **LISTENING 5** **SPEAKING** Listen and answer the questions. Then write your answers below.

What's your name?

My name's ...

1 My name's ...
2 I'm seventeen
3 I'm ...
4 T–A–N–...
5 I'm from Ukraine

6 Write a dialogue like the one in exercise 1. Use the information in the chart below.

Name: Susannah	Name: Alessia	Name: Baykal
Age: 17	Age: 16	Age: 16
	From: Italy	From: Turkey

Susannah Hi, Alessia. How are you?
Alessia   Fine thanks, Susannah ...
Susannah I'm fine too, Alessia this is Baykal. He's from Turkey
Alessia   Hi nice to meet you
Baykal   How you from ... you from
Alessia   I'm ...
Baykal
Alessia   I'm seventeen ... and you ...
Baykal
Alessia   How do you spell your name
Baykal   B–A–Y...

I can ask and answer questions.

1 Complete the sentences. Use the affirmative form of *be*.

1 You _are_ from Australia.
2 My English teacher _is_ Mr Simpson.
3 Tom and Betty _____ in my class.
4 I _____ seventeen years old.
5 My pencil _____ in my bag.
6 We _are_ at home.

2 Write sentences. Use the negative form of *be*.

1 This coffee / hot
   This coffee isn't hot.
2 Sam / in the classroom
   Sam isn't in the classroom
3 We / eighteen years old
   We aren't eighteen years old
4 They / from New Zealand
   They aren't from New Zealand
5 I / hungry
   I'm not hungry.

3 Put the words in the correct order to make questions. Then match the questions with answers a–f below.

1 Martin / name / your / is / ?
   Is your name Martin? ☐
2 you / are / Ireland / from / ?
   Are you from Ireland? ☐
3 at / home / is / dad / your / ?
   Is your dad at home? ☐
4 teachers / and Harry / are / Neil / ?
   Are Neil and Harry teachers? ☐
5 Joanna / and I / American / are / ?
   Are Joanna and I American? ☐
6 Sarah / is / hungry / ?
   Is Sarah hungry? ☐

a Yes, he is.   c No, it isn't.   e Yes, we are.
b No, they aren't.   d Yes, she is.   f Yes, I am.

4 🎧 LISTENING 6 Look at the information in the chart. Then listen to six sentences. Are they true (T) or false (F)?

Name	Liam	Clare
Age	18	19
City / country	New York, USA	Chicago, USA
Favourite food	pizza	ice cream

1	F	2		3	F	4		5		6	F

5 Write true short answers.

1 Is your English teacher a man? Yes, he is
2 Is your Workbook green? Yes, it is
3 Is yellow your favourite colour? No, it's not
4 Are your school friends British? No, they aren't
5 Are you at school? No, I'm not

6 Write the possessive adjectives for the personal pronouns.

1 I _my_   5 it _its_
2 you _your_   6 we _our_
3 he _his_   7 you _your_
4 she _her_   8 they _their_

7 Match 1–6 with pictures a–f below. Complete the sentences with *this*, *that*, *these* and *those*.

1 ... is my mum.   4 ... are our sisters.
2 ~~... are your pens.~~   5 ... is my schoolbag.
3 ... is his bike.   6 ... are our books.

a These are your pens.   b That is my mum
c These are our sisters   d This is my schoolbag
e That is his bike   f These are our books

Challenge!

Write four more true sentences about you, your family and friends.

1 I'm from Ukraine. My mum is from
2 My brother is 5 years old
3 I have two daughters.
4 These names are made up
5 I'm fourteen years old

IC GRAMMAR *have got* and articles

I can talk about possessions.

1 Complete the message. Use the affirmative form of *have got*.

Hi! My name is Isaac and I'm a big Manchester United fan, like my dad. I ¹ *have got* posters of the players in my bedroom and my dad ² *has got* lots of books about the team. He ³ *has got* some old magazines about football too. I really like them – they ⁴_____ amazing photos of players from the 1950s. We ⁵ *have got* a dog. Its name is Rooney!

2 Complete the first part of sentences 1–6 with the negative form of *have got*. Then match them with the second part a–f.

1 I _haven't got_ a TV in my room, but   ☐ c
2 We _____ a Ferrari, but   ☐ f
3 She _____ brothers or sisters, but   ☐ a
4 They _____ a piano at home, but   ☐ e
5 He _____ a bike, but   ☐
6 I _____ a computer, but   ☐

a she's got cousins.
b I've got a phone.
c I've got a radio.
d he's got a skateboard.
e they've got a guitar.
f we've got a Porsche.

3 Look at the chart. Write questions and short answers about Emily and her brother Leo. Use *have got*.

	Emily	Leo
🎸	✓	✗
🐱	✗	✗
📖	✓	✓
🎧	✗	✓

1 Emily / a guitar?
   Has Emily got a guitar? Yes, she has.
2 Leo / a guitar?
   Has Leo got a guitar? No, he hasn't
3 Emily and Leo / a cat?
   Have Emily and Leo got a cat? No, they haven't
4 Emily and Leo / a dictionary?
   Have Emily and Leo got a dictionary? Yes, they have
5 Emily / an MP3 player?
   Has Emily got an MP3 player? No, she hasn't
6 Leo / an MP3 player?
   Has Leo got an MP3 player? Yes, he has

4 Write *a* or *an*.

1 It's _an_ old dictionary.
2 Have you got _an_ MP3 player?
3 I've got all my photos on _a_ CD.
4 He hasn't got _a_ girlfriend.
5 This is _an_ amazing garden.
6 It's _a_ beautiful afternoon.

5 Complete the dialogue with *a*, *an* or *the*.

Nathan Have you got ¹ _a_ dog?
Leah Yes, I have. I've got ² _a_ cat too.
Nathan What are their names?
Leah ³ _The_ dog's name is Blackie and ⁴ _the_ cat's name is Penfold.
Nathan Where are they now?
Leah They're in ⁵ _the_ garden.
Nathan Oh, yes. Look! Blackie has got ⁶ _an_ old shoe.
Leah Hey! That's one of my new trainers!

6 Choose the correct answers.

1 'What's on _radio_ ?' 'A Lady Gaga song.'
   a a radio   **b the radio**   c radio
2 'When's our guitar lesson?' 'In _the afternoon_.'
   a an afternoon   **b the afternoon**   c afternoon
3 Is Alex at _home_ today?
   a a home   b the home   **c home**
4 My cat is always awake at _night_ .
   a a night   b the night   **c night**
5 Wow! You've got _an amazing_ bike!
   a an amazing   b the amazing   c amazing

Challenge!

Write three affirmative and three negative sentences about you, your family and friends. Use *have got*.

1 I haven't got a cat
2 The cat's name is Blackie
3 I have got two dogs
4 I haven't got a dog
5 He haven't got a ball
6 My neighbours haven't got a piano

VOCABULARY Time, days and dates

I can ask the time and talk about dates.

1 🎧 **LISTENING 7** Listen to the dialogues. Draw the times on the clocks.

|1| |2| |3|
|4| |5| |6|

2 Write the times from exercise 1.

1 It's half past three.
2 It's five to seven
3 It's quarter past seven
4 It's half past
5 It's twenty to
6 It's ten o'clock

3 Put the words in the correct order. Then complete the dialogue with the sentences.

half / ten / it's / past
is / time / please / what / it, / ?
welcome / you're
you / thank

A Excuse me. ¹ What time is it, please?
B ² I
A ³ T
B ⁴ Y

4 Write the days of the week in the correct order.

1 Sunday
2 Monday
3 T
4 W
5 T
6 F
7 S

5 Find eleven more months of the year in the wordsearch. Then write the twelve months in the correct order.

Q	W	M	A	R	C	H	E	R	J	T	Y
U	J	I	O	P	A	A	U	G	U	S	T
M	A	Y	S	S	D	F	F	G	L	H	J
K	N	O	V	E	M	B	E	R	Y	O	D
J	U	N	E	P	L	Z	B	X	C	C	E
V	A	B	N	T	A	P	R	I	L	T	C
M	R	Q	W	E	E	R	U	T	Y	O	E
U	Y	I	O	M	P	A	A	S	D	B	M
F	G	H	J	B	K	L	R	L	Z	E	B
X	C	V	B	E	N	M	Y	Q	W	R	E
E	R	T	Y	R	U	I	O	P	A	S	R

1 January   5 May   9 September
2 February   6 June   10 October
3 March   7 July   11 November
4 April   8 August   12 December

6 Write the words.

1st first   7th
2nd   8th
3rd   9th
4th   10th
5th   11th
6th   12th

7 Write the numbers.

1 twenty-third 23rd   4 thirty-first   31st
2 fifteenth   5 eighteenth   18th
3 thirtieth   6 twenty-second

8 🎧 **LISTENING 8** Listen and write the dates.

1 23rd May
2 1st June
3 19th December
4 20th January
5 31st July
6 February
7 8th September
8 6th March

1A VOCABULARY Family

I can describe my family.

1 Do the crossword.

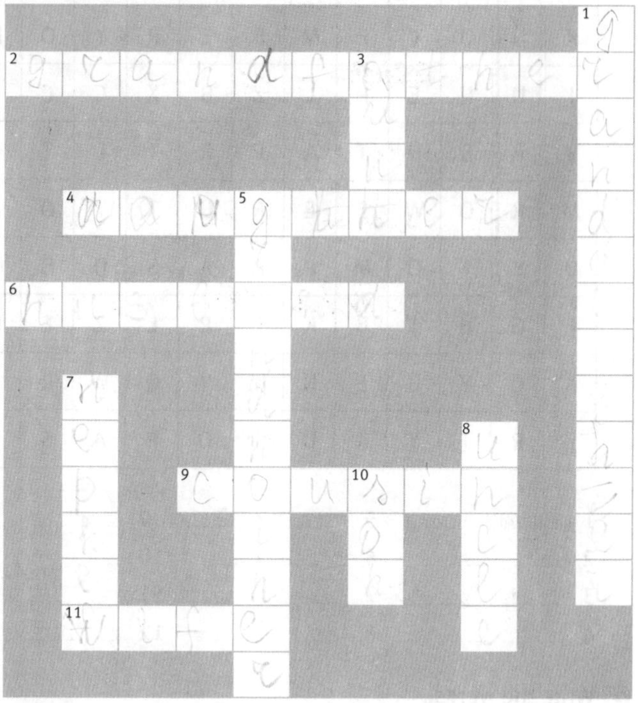

Crossword (handwritten answers):
- 1 (down) g...
- 2 (across) g r a n d f a t h e r
- 4 (across) d a u g h t e r
- 6 (across) h u s b a n d
- 9 (across) c o u s i n
- 11 (across) w i f e

Across
2 My mother's father is my _grandfather_.
4 My son's sister is my _daughter_.
6 I'm his wife, he's my _husband_.
9 My uncle's daughter is my _cousin_.
11 I'm her husband, she's my _wife_.

Down
1 My son's daughter is my _granddaughter_.
3 My cousin's mother is my _aunt_.
5 My father's mother is my _____.
7 My brother's son is my _____.
8 My dad's brother is my _____.
10 My daughter's brother is my _____.

2 Write the missing words.
1 sons + daughters = _children_
2 mother + father = _____
3 grandmother + grandfather = _grandparents_
4 grandson + _____ = _____
5 _____ + _____ = great-grandparents

3 Match 1–6 with a–f.
1 I'm his stepsister. [f]   a She's my niece.
2 I'm his twin. [ ]   b He's my twin.
3 I'm her uncle. [ ]   c She's my cousin.
4 I'm her stepmother. [ ]   d She's my stepdaughter.
5 I'm her cousin. [ ]   e He's my nephew.
6 I'm his aunt. [ ]   f He's my stepbrother.

4 Rewrite each pair of sentences as one sentence. Use possessive 's.
1 John has got a bike. It's new.
   John's bike is _____ new.
2 My cousins live in a flat. It's very big.
   My cousins' _____ very big.
3 Naomi has got a computer. It's new.
   Naomi's computer is _____ new.
4 My friends are having a party. It's on Saturday.
   My friends' _____ Saturday.
5 Her grandparents have got a cat. It's black.
   Her grandparents' cat is _____ black.

VOCABULARY BUILDER (PART 2): PLURAL FORMS OF NOUNS. ≫SB PAGE 131≪

5 Write the plural form of the nouns in the correct column.

box   brother   bus   dish   match   photo   tomato   twin   uncle   video

+ -s brothers	+ -es boxes
photos, videos, tomatoes, twins, uncles	buses, dishes, matches

6 Complete the sentences with plural form of the nouns.
1 My aunt has got three _children_ (child).
2 Those _babies_ (baby) haven't got any _teeth_ (tooth).
3 Four _men_ (man) and four _women_ (woman) are in the team.
4 Two _families_ (family) live in that house.
5 There are six _persons_ (person) in my family.

1B GRAMMAR Present simple: affirmative and negative

I can talk about facts and things that happen regularly.

1 Complete the sentences. Use the present simple affirmative form of the verbs in brackets.

1 My aunt and uncle _____live_____ (live) in the USA.
2 Rosie _____has_____ (have) music lessons every weekend.
3 My best friend _____plays_____ (play) in the school basketball team.
4 I _____study_____ (study) Russian at school.
5 My cousin and I _____like_____ (like) football.
6 My stepbrother _____ (watch) TV every night.

2 Complete the sentences. Use the present simple affirmative form of the verbs in the box.

come get up have meet speak work

1 My sister _____has_____ Japanese lessons at weekends.
2 Ellie's parents _____work_____ at a hospital in the USA.
3 My neighbour _____comes_____ from France.
4 We _____meet_____ friends in town every Saturday evening.
5 I _____get up_____ late on Sundays.
6 My grandfather _____speaks_____ four languages.

3 What do they do on Saturdays and Sundays? Look at the chart and write sentences about the activities.

	Saturdays	Sundays
Tom	pizza	TV
Sofia	$5a(1-x^2)=16$	music
Hannah and Sam	tennis	music

1 play tennis
   Hannah and Sam play tennis on Saturdays.
2 study maths
   Sofia studies maths on Saturdays
3 eat pizza
   Tom eats pizza on Saturdays
4 watch TV
   Tom watches TV on Sundays
5 listen to music
   Hannah and Sam listen to music on Sundays
6 go out
   Sofia goes out on Sundays.

4 Put the words in the correct order to make sentences.

1 sister / go out / my / doesn't / a lot
   My sister doesn't go out a lot.
2 New York / parents / live / in / don't / Tom's
   Tom's parents don't live in New York
3 pizza / brother / eat / doesn't / my
   My brother doesn't eat pizza
4 teacher / our / doesn't / work / Sundays / on
   Our teacher doesn't work on Sundays
5 Lady Gaga / like / my / don't / parents
   My parents don't like Lady Gaga
6 Chinese / Sam / speak / doesn't
   Sam doesn't speak Chinese
7 friends / Elizabeth's / like / we / don't
   We don't like Elizabeth's friends

5 Make the sentences negative.

1 I live in a big house.
   I don't live in a big house.
2 My dad works in a hotel.
   My dad doesn't work in a hotel
3 My friends like sport.
   My friends don't like sport
4 My best friend speaks Japanese.
   My best friend doesn't speak Japanese
5 We go to school on Saturdays.
   We don't go to school on Saturdays.
6 My brother has guitar lessons.
   My brother doesn't have guitar lessons
7 My grandmother watches TV all day.
   My grandmother doesn't watch TV all day.

Challenge!

Write six sentences about your family and friends. Use the present simple affirmative or negative. Choose from the verbs in the box.

get up go like live play speak study work

My dad likes ice hockey.
My cousin Anna doesn't live in this country.
1 My husband get up early everyday
2 I go to the store on Fridays
3 My daughter don't like sport
4 She speaks three languages
5 We don't live in Ukraine
6 He doesn't work, but he studies

Revision: Student's Book page 10

1 Complete the facts about the UK with the words in the box.

elections	government	laws	parties	queen

1 The three main _partieí_ in the UK are the Conservatives, Labour and the Liberal Democrats.
2 Elizabeth II is the _qeen_ , but her husband, Prince Philip, is not a king.
3 In the UK, _election_ are always on a Thursday.
4 Inside the House of Commons, the _laws_ sits on one side of the room and the other MPs sit on the other side.
5 British MPs vote on new _goverment_ every year.

2 Read the text. Are the sentences true (T) or false (F)?

1 There are four Royal garden parties at Buckingham Palace every year. **F**
2 The Royal Family chooses all of the guests. **F**
3 The parties start at 3 p.m. and finish at 6 p.m. **T**
4 The guests drink tea, but they don't drink coffee. **F**
5 The guests take photos of the Queen at the garden parties. **F**
6 The Queen and her husband go to all of the garden parties. **T**

3 🎧 LISTENING 9 Listen to three people talking about Royal garden parties. Match sentences a–c with speakers 1–3.

a This person helps to decide who goes to the parties. **2**
b This person asks guests some questions. **3**
c This person prepares food for the parties. **1**

Challenge!

Complete sentences 1–5 with the names of the people. Try to add one more.

1 The Prime Minister of the UK is _Boris Jonson_
2 The President of the USA is _Donald TRAMP_
3 The President of Germany is _____ .
4 The King of Spain is _____
5 The _president_ of my country is _Vladimir Zelen_
6 The _qeen_ of _the UK_ is _Elizabeth II_ .

Tea and cakes

There are four Royal garden parties every year – one in Scotland and three at Buckingham Palace in London. About 8,000 people go to each party. The government and many different charities all help to choose the guests.

The party starts at three o'clock in the afternoon. The guests listen to music (there are two bands) and walk around the beautiful gardens. They drink tea or coffee and eat sandwiches and cakes. They can't take photos or use mobile phones.

At four o'clock, the Queen and her husband, the Duke of Edinburgh, join the party. Other members of the Royal Family – like Prince Charles, Prince William and Princess Anne – don't go to every garden party, but they go to one or two a year. It's a chance for the Royal Family to meet and talk to the public. The party finishes at six o'clock.

GRAMMAR # Present simple: questions

I can ask questions about facts and everyday events.

1 Complete the questions and short answers. Use *do*, *don't*, *does* and *doesn't*.

1 _Does_ your dad work in town?
No, he _doesn't_ .

2 _Do_ your cousins live near the school?
Yes, they _do_ .

3 _Do_ lessons start at nine o'clock?
No, they _don't_ .

4 _Do_ you like computers?
No, I _don't_ .

5 _Does_ the Queen live at Buckingham Palace?
Yes, she _does_ .

6 _Do_ you drink coffee?
Yes, I _do_ .

2 Look at the chart. Then write questions and answers about Edward and Rosie.

	Edward	Rosie
live in an apartment	✓	✓
work in London	✓	✗
speak Spanish	✗	✓
like cooking	✗	✗
play football	✓	✗
go out a lot	✓	✓

1 Edward / live in an apartment?
Does Edward live in an apartment?
Yes, he does.

2 Rosie / live in an apartment?
Does Rosie live in an apartment?
Yes, she does.

3 Rosie / work in London?
Does Rosie work in London?
Yes, she does.

4 Edward / speak Spanish?
Does Edward speak Spanish?
No, he doesn't

5 Rosie and Edward / like cooking?
Do Rosie and Edward like cooking?
No, they don't

6 Edward / play football?
Does Edward play football?
Yes, he does

7 Rosie and Edward / go out a lot?
Do Rosie and Edward go out a lot?
Yes, they do

3 Put the words in the correct order to make questions.

1 does / your / live / cousin / where / ?
Where does your cousin live?

2 like / do / why / Angelina Jolie / you / ?
Why do you like Angelina Jolie?

3 lunch / you / when / do / have / ?
When do you have lunch?

4 do / sports / they / do / which / ?
Which sports do they do?

5 you / for / what / dinner / do / want / ?
What do you want for dinner?

6 with / who / live / you / do / ?
Who do you live with?

4 Match these answers with the questions in exercise 3.

a [6] My parents.
b [5] Pasta, please.
c [1] In Scotland.
d [2] Because she's beautiful!
e [4] Football and tennis.
f [3] At one o'clock.

Challenge!

Write the questions. Use the question words in the box. Then write true answers.

how	what	where	who

1 you / live
Where do you live?
I live in Scotland

2 your best friend / travel to school
How does your best friend travel to school?
My best friend travels to school by bus.

3 you / sit next to in class
Who do you sit next to in class?
Max sits next to me in class.

4 you / have for breakfast
What do you have for breakfast?
I have a fry eggs for breakfast

I can understand an article about a community.

Revision: Student's Book page 12

1 Complete the sentences. Use the affirmative form of the verbs in the box.

| do finish get go go have prepare |
| start use |

1 My sister _goes_ to bed at 9 p.m. on Sundays.
2 We _have_ lunch at school during the week.
3 Our teachers _use_ computers in the classroom.
4 My grandfather _does_ the housework at weekends.
5 I _get_ up at 7 a.m. from Monday to Friday.
6 My sister _goes_ to school by train.
7 I work in a restaurant. I _prepare_ food.
8 My dad _starts_ work at 6 a.m. and he _finishes_ work at 2 p.m.

2 Read the text. Which of these things do the members of the Long Hill community have? Tick ✓ or cross ✗.

☑ animals   ☑ books
☑ houses   ☒ computers
☒ TVs   ☑ phones

Life at Long Hill

The Long Hill Community is a group of twenty families who live together in the south of England. They have a small farm with animals and ten small houses. Two families live in each house. Their aim is to live without the help of modern technology.

The adults at Long Hill don't have jobs outside the Community, but they work very hard. They get up early and they have breakfast. Then they start work on the farm or they do housework. The children have lessons in the morning. Their teachers are all members of the Community.

'We don't hate technology,' says Martin Edwards, the founder of the Community, 'but we want a simple, natural life. And technology isn't simple – or natural!' So at Long Hill, they don't use computers or watch TV. They haven't got phones. So what do they do in the evenings? 'Lots of things: we read books, we play games, we play music and sing,' says Martin. 'Life at Long Hill is simple, but it's never boring.'

3 Choose the best answers.

1 Each family in the Long Hill Community
  (a) lives with another family.
  b has got animals.
  c has got two houses.
2 All the adults in the Community
  a are teachers.
  b have got jobs outside the Community.
  (c) work inside the Community.
3 In the morning, the children
  (a) have lessons.
  b work on the farm.
  c do housework.
4 At Long Hill, they don't use modern technology because
  a they hate it.
  (b) they want a natural life.
  c they don't understand it.
5 In the evening, the families at Long Hill
  a watch films.
  (b) enjoy music.
  c play computer games.

Challenge!

Write three questions to ask the people who live in the Long Hill Community. Use the topics in the box or your own ideas.

| exams   food   sports   university |

1 Who prepares food in the Community?
2 Which sports do they do?
3 Do children take university lessons/exams?

EVERYDAY ENGLISH Introducing people

I can introduce myself to new people.

1 Put the words in the correct order to make questions.

a in / you / what / class / are / ?
What class are you in? ?

b you / from / are / where / ?
Where are you from ?

c near / you / school / the / do / live / ?
Do you live near the school ?

d brothers / you / any / got / have / sisters / or / ?
Have you got any brothers or sisters ?

e day / first / this / at / school / this / your / is / ?
Is this your first day at school ?

f got / have / friends / this / school / at / you / ?
Have you got friends at this school ?

2 🎧 LISTENING 10 Complete the dialogue with questions a–f from exercise 1. Then listen and check.

Lucas   Hi, I'm Lucas.
Sienna Nice to meet you. I'm Sienna.
Lucas   ¹ e
Sienna Yes, it is.
Lucas   ² a
Sienna I'm in 11B.
Lucas   Oh, really? My friend Reece is in that class. ³ f
Sienna No, I haven't. I don't know anybody!
Lucas   ⁴ d
Sienna Yes, I've got a brother called Theo. He's 20. He's at university back home.
Lucas   ⁵ b
Sienna We're from Scotland. But my mum has got a new job.
Lucas   ⁶ c
Sienna Yes, we do. But I don't like our new house!

3 Look at the dialogue in exercise 2 again and complete the fact file about Sienna.

Name:	Sienna	From:	Scotland
Family:	(brother / sister)		brother Theo
	(age)		20
	(school / job / university)		university

4 Match the object pronouns with the subject pronouns.

I	it
you	we
he	you
she	they

her	him
us	them
you	you
me	it

5 Complete the sentences with subject or object pronouns from exercise 4.

1 What do you think of Lady Gaga's songs? Do you like _them_ ?
2 We go to Spain every year because _we_ really like it.
3 Jack and Amelia are at this school. Do you know _them_ ?
4 I speak to Sophia every day. She phones _me_ before school.
5 Do you know my parents? _They_ work in the hospital.
6 Your sister Lucy is in my class at school. I sit next to _her_ .
7 Do you like basketball? Yes, I love _it_ .
8 My dad walks to work and my mum goes with _him_ .

6 🎧 LISTENING 11 Listen to the dialogue. Then complete the fact file about Emily.

Name:	Emily	From:	USA
Family:	(brother / sister)		sister
	(age)		
	(school / job / university)		

7 Invent a fact file for Finley, a new student at your school.

Name:	Finley	From:	Germany
Family:	(brother / sister)		brother
	(age)		25
	(school / job / university)		job

8 Write a dialogue like the one in exercise 2. Use the information about Finley in exercise 7.

You   Hi, I'm _____ .
Finley Nice _to meet you. I'm Finley_ .
You   Is _this your first day at this school_ ?
Finley _Yes_ .
You   What _class are you in_ ?
Finley I'm _in 11A_ .
You   Have _you got friends_ ?
Finley _No, I don't know anybody_
You   Have _you got brothers or sisters_ ?
Finley Yes. I've got _a brother called Max. He works in the office_
You   Where _are you from_ ?
Finley _I'm from Germany_
You   Do _they live near the school_ ?
Finley _No, I don't_

Preparation

1 Read the message. Are the sentences true (T) or false (F)?

a Callum is new to the school. ☐

b Callum is new to London. T

c Callum is not new to the school or London. F

Hi! My name is Callum and I'm sixteen. I'm in class 11D. I come from Canada. I've got two sisters, Lexi and Maddison. They're at the school too, so I already know two people here! We live with our mum and dad in a small flat here in London. It's near the school, so we walk to school every morning. I really like London, but I miss our big house in Canada.

I love sport. At home in Canada, I play ice hockey. Here in London, I play basketball. I don't play football, but I watch it on TV. I also watch DVDs a lot. My favourite actor is Jackie Chan.

2 What information about Callum is in his message? Tick ✓ the correct paragraph (1 or 2), or tick ✓ 'Not there'.

	Para 1	Para 2	Not there
his name	✓		
his hobbies		✓	
his pets			✓
his age	✓		
his favourite actor		✓	
his favourite sports team		✓	
where he lives	✓		
his class at school	✓		
his favourite singer			✓

3 Match 1–6 with a–f to make sentences.

1 I come from ☐   a Julia.

2 I've got ☐   b fifteen years old.

3 My name is ☐   c basketball.

4 I play ☐   d Oxford.

5 I'm ☐   e my parents and my brother.

6 I live with ☐   f a brother and a sister.

4 Complete the messages with the prepositions in the box. You can use the prepositions more than once.

at by for in on to with

1 The new Ben Affleck film is _on_ TV _at_ nine o'clock tonight. Do you want to watch it _with_ me?

2 My dad isn't _at_ home. He's _in_ China _for_ two weeks.

3 I'm _on_ the bus. Are you _at_ school?

4 I'm _in_ town. Do you want pizza _for_ dinner tonight?

5 I go _to_ school _by_ bus. I sit _with_ my friends and we listen _to_ music.

Writing guide

5 Imagine you are a new student at your school. Write a message for the school magazine to introduce yourself. Follow the guide below.

1 Give your name and age.

2 Say what class you are in.

3 Say where you are from.

4 Talk about your family and your home.

5 Talk about one of your hobbies.

6 Mention a favourite (team, singer, actor, etc.)

7 Talk about another hobby or interest.

Hi! ¹ _my name is ..._
² _I'm in class ..._
³ _I come from ..._
⁴ _I've got a sister ..._
she's at there ... we live with our parents named ...
⁵ _I like swimming and dancing. I also watch ..._
⁶ _my favourite ..._
⁷ _I like to go ..._

1 Write the family members.

1 My aunt's husband is my _uncle_ .
2 My aunt's daughter is my _cousin_ .
3 My father's father is my _grandfather_ .
4 My brother's son is my _____ .
5 My sister's daughter is my _____ .
6 My son's children are my _____ children_ .
7 My mother's parents are my _grandparents_ .
8 My father's sister is my _aunt_ .

Mark: _8_ /8

2 Complete the sentences with the plural form of the nouns in the box.

| bus child photo shelf university woman |

1 Oxford and Cambridge are two _universities_ in England.
2 Which _buses_ go to the town centre?
3 Lady Gaga and Angelina Jolie are famous _women_ .
4 Look at these _photos_ of my holiday!
5 My aunt and uncle have got five _children_ .
6 Please put all the books on the _shelves_ .

Mark: _6_ /6

3 Complete the sentences. Use the present simple affirmative form of the verbs in brackets.

1 My parents _get up_ early on Sundays. (get up)
2 Anna _watches_ TV in her bedroom. (watch)
3 My brother and I _speak_ five languages. (speak)
4 You _____ tomatoes. (like)
5 My sister _has_ swimming lessons. (have)

Mark: _5_ /5

4 Rewrite the sentences in exercise 3. Use the present simple negative form of the verbs.

1 _____
2 _____
3 _____
4 _____
5 _____

Mark: _5_ /5

5 Write the questions and complete the short answers. Use the present simple.

1 Anna / play tennis ?
Does Anna play tennis ?
Yes, _she does_ .

2 your cousins / live near here ?
Do your cousins live near here ?
No, _they don't_ .

3 your dad / speak French ?
Do your dad speak French ?
No, _he doesn't_ .

4 Mike and Andy / have music lessons ?
Do Mike and Andy have music lessons ?
Yes, _they do_ .

5 you and your friends / go out a lot ?
Do you and your friends go out a lot ?
No, _we don't_ .

6 you / like sport ?
Do you like sport ?
Yes, _I do_ .

Mark: _6_ /6

Total: _____ /30

I can ...

Read the statements. Think about your progress and tick one of the boxes.

✱ = I need more practice.   ✱✱ = I sometimes find this difficult.

✱✱✱ = No problem!

	✱	✱✱	✱✱✱
I can describe my family. (SB p.8)		✓	
I can talk about facts and things that happen regularly. (SB p.9)		✓	
I can talk about the monarchy. (SB p.10)	✓		
I can ask questions about facts and everyday events. (SB p.11)		✓	
I can understand an article about a community. (SB p.12)		✓	
I can introduce myself to new people. (SB p.14)		✓	
I can write a message about myself. (SB p.15)		✓	

2A VOCABULARY Free-time activities

I can talk about my hobbies.

1 Label the pictures.

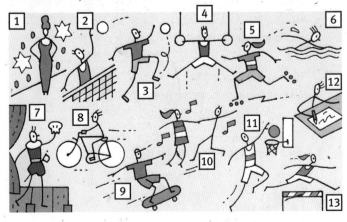

1 f _oto odel_
2 v _olleyball_
3 f _oo ba_
4 g _im as_
5 r _o ero ... ing_
6 s _ imming_
7 d _ramati_

8 c _ ...
9 s _ ...
10 d _ ...
11 b _ ...
12 d _ ...
13 a _ ...

2 Complete the activities with the words in the box.

books films games games hockey jogging
magazines photos skating the Net to music

1 listening _to mus_
2 video _ ..._
3 ice _hockey_
4 board _games_
5 ice _skating_
6 going _jogging_

7 reading _b ..._
8 surfing _the Net_
9 watching _film_
10 reading _magazines_
11 taking _ ..._

3 Write three true sentences about the activities in exercises 1 and 2. Use the phrases in the box.

I'm really into   I really like   I quite like
I'm not very keen on   I don't like

1 I _really like swimming_ ,
   but I _don't like ice ..._
2 I _'m really into dancing_ ,
   but I _'m not very keen on ..._
3 I _quite like video games_ ,
   but I _really be ..._

VOCABULARY BUILDER (PART 2): VERB + NOUN COLLOCATIONS. >>SB PAGE 132<<

4 Complete the sentences. Use the present simple form of *do, play* or *go.*

1 Liam _does_ gymnastics on Friday evenings.
2 I _play_ basketball after school.
3 We don't _do_ athletics at school.
4 My sister _does_ karate.
5 Jason _g_ skateboarding with his friends.
6 My cousin _plays_ tennis on Sundays.
7 I don't _go_ ice skating very often.
8 My friends and I _go_ rollerblading in the park.

5 Choose the correct words.

1 I'm not very keen on **watching** / **doing** sport on TV.
2 They go for **a film** / **a walk** on Saturday mornings.
3 My dad likes surfing **the computer** / **the Net.**
4 I **watch** / **play** video games with my brother.
5 We read **magazines** / **DVDs** at home.
6 I don't **do** / **play** a musical instrument.
7 We do **athletics** / **volleyball** at school.
8 My sister **plays** / **does** gymnastics.

Challenge!

Write a paragraph about your free-time activities. Use the phrases in the box to help you.

at weekends   in the evening
on Sunday morning/afternoon

I ... tennis at weekends.
I do exercise on Sunday
mo ning
I like reading boo s in the
evening

2B GRAMMAR Adverbs of frequency

I can say how often something happens.

1 Complete the adverbs of frequency with *a, e, i, o* and *u*.

1 n_v_r (ne v e r)
2 s_m_t_m_s (sometimes)
3 _s___lly (usually)
4 _lw_ys (always)
5 h_rdly _v_r (hardly ever)
6 _ft_n (often)

2 Complete the chart with the adverbs of frequency in exercise 1.

1	always	■ ■ ■ ■ ■
2	_	■ ■ ■ ■ □
3	_	■ ■ ■ □ □
4	_	■ ■ □ □ □
5	hardly ever	■ □ □ □ □
6	_	□ □ □ □ □

3 Put the words in the correct order to make sentences.

1 often / on Sundays. / has / breakfast / in bed / Mike
   Mike often has breakfast in bed on Sundays.

2 go shopping / sometimes / on Saturdays. / I
   _____

3 is / on Friday evenings. / at home / Kate / never
   _____

4 speaks / in our English lessons. / always / our teacher / English
   _____

5 at school. / usually / am / I / hungry
   _____

6 Ben and Jake / books. / hardly ever / read
   _____

4 Write sentences about Sam. Add the correct adverb of frequency.

1 get up at seven o'clock ■ ■ ■ ■ ■
   Sam always gets up at seven o'clock.

2 watch TV after school ■ □ □ □ □
   Sam _____

3 be late for school ■ ■ ■ □ □
   _____

4 be in bed before eleven o'clock □ □ □ □ □
   _____

5 tidy his bedroom at the weekend ■ ■ □ □ □
   _____

6 do the washing-up ■ ■ ■ ■ □
   _____

5 Rewrite the sentences in exercise 4 so that they are true for you.

1 I _____ get up at seven o'clock.
2 _____
3 _____
4 _____
5 _____
6 _____

6 🎧 LISTENING 12 Listen to Joe saying what he does on Saturdays. Tick ✓ the correct boxes in the chart.

	always	usually	often	sometimes	hardly ever	never
do my homework					✓	
play football	✓					
watch TV			✓			
listen to music						
go dancing						

7 Write questions about Joe with *How often*. Then answer them with an adverb of frequency.

1 Joe / do his homework on Saturdays?
   How often does Joe do his homework on Saturdays?
   Hardly ever.

2 Joe / play football on Saturdays?
   _____

3 Joe / watch television on Saturdays?
   _____

4 Joe / listen to music on Saturdays?
   _____

5 Joe / go dancing on Saturdays?
   _____

Challenge!

Write three more questions for your classmates with *How often*.

1 How often do you play football?
2 _____
3 _____

I can understand different views on activities.

Revision: Student's Book page 20

1 Choose the correct words.

I'm a ¹fan / crowd of Chelsea football club. I often go and see them play. The ²match / goal between Chelsea and Manchester United is always exciting. The ³crowd / fan always cheers when Chelsea scores a ⁴team / goal. I think Chelsea is the best football ⁵fan / team in the world!

2 Complete the text with the verbs in the box.

are   is   learn   train   watch   win

BALLROOM DANCING

Ballroom dancing ¹_____ over 400 years old, but the modern dance steps are from England in the 1920s. It's very popular and is a hobby for people of all ages. But is ballroom dancing a sport? Ballroom dancers ²_____ a lot, and they enter competitions. The most important competition is in Blackpool, in the north of England. Dancers from all over the world compete there every year to ³_____ the dance championship.

TV programmes about ballroom dancing ⁴_____ very popular. In *Strictly Come Dancing*, a British TV programme, celebrities dance with professional dancers. Every week the celebrities ⁵_____ a new dance and after the show, people vote for their favourite celebrity dancer. In Britain, about thirteen million people ⁶_____ the final on TV every year!

3 Read the text again. Choose the correct answers.

1 Ballroom dancing is
   a about forty years old.
   b about eighty years old.
   c about four hundred years old.
2 Ballroom dancers
   a are usually young.
   b are usually old.
   c are young or old.
3 The championship in Blackpool is
   a only for dancers from outside the UK.
   b for dancers from many countries.
   c only for dancers from England.
4 In *Strictly Come Dancing*, professional dancers
   a compete against other professional dancers.
   b compete with celebrities.
   c compete against celebrities.
5 Every year, thirteen million people
   a vote for their favourite *Strictly Come Dancing* show.
   b watch the final of *Strictly Come Dancing*.
   c want to compete in *Strictly Come Dancing*.

4 🎧 LISTENING 13 Listen to the radio programme. Are the sentences true (T) or false (F)?

1 Nick and Shelley are dance champions. `T`
2 They train five times a week. `F`
3 Nick is Shelley's boyfriend. `F`
4 They compete in four or five competitions every year. `T`
5 Their next competition is next year. `F`

Challenge!

Write a short text (3–5 sentences) about a TV show you like, or a popular competition in your country.

_____
_____
_____
_____
_____
_____
_____
_____
_____
_____
_____
_____

2D GRAMMAR *can* and adverbs

I can say how well I can do something.

1 Look at the chart. Complete the sentences below with *can* or *can't* and verbs or phrases from the chart.

	Jack	Chloe	James
play the guitar	✓	✓	✓
ride a motorbike	✓	✓	✗
ride a horse	✓	✗	✗
speak Italian	✓	✗	✓

1 Jack _can play_ the guitar and he _can ride_ a horse.

2 Chloe _____ a motorbike, but she _can't ride_ a horse.

3 James _____ Italian and he _____ the guitar.

4 Jack and James _____, but Chloe can't.

5 James and Chloe _____, but Jack can.

6 James _____ a motorbike, but Chloe and Jack _can_ .

7 Jack, Chloe and James _can play the guitar_ .

2 What can you do? Write questions and true answers with *can*.

1 cook

Can you cook?

Yes, I can. / No, I can't.

2 play a musical instrument

_____

_____

3 ride a bike

_____

_____

4 speak Russian

_____

_____

5 write songs

_____

6 swim 100 metres

_____

7 sing

_____

_____

8 read people's thoughts

_____

_____

3 Write the adverbs.

1 slow _slowly_

2 early _____

3 hard _hardly_

4 careful _carefully_

5 good _well_

6 loud _____

7 easy _____

8 fast _____

9 beautiful _____

10 fluent _____

11 late _____

12 bad _____

4 Choose the correct adjective or adverb to complete the sentences.

1 He's a **slow** / **slowly** driver.

2 Please listen **careful** / **carefully**.

3 Vicky has got a **loud** / **loudly** voice.

4 Jake learns very **quick** / **quickly**.

5 Anna is a **beautiful** / **beautifully** dancer.

6 Can you speak Russian **fluent** / **fluently**?

5 Write sentences. Use the present simple and an adverb.

1 Emma's dad / dance / bad

Emma's dad dances badly.

2 Tom / speak French / fluent

_____

3 Peter / play the piano / good

_____

4 William and Kate / get up / early

_____

5 Oliver / sing / loud

_____

6 Holly / learn new vocabulary / easy

_____

7 Jo's uncle / drive / careful

_____

8 Ellen and Martin / swim / fast

_____

Challenge!

DICTIONARY WORK Write the adverbs from these adjectives. Check your answers in a dictionary.

1 sad _____

2 happy _____

3 quiet _____

4 angry _____

5 nice _____

6 sudden _suddenly_

Revision: Student's Book page 22

1 Label the parts of the body.

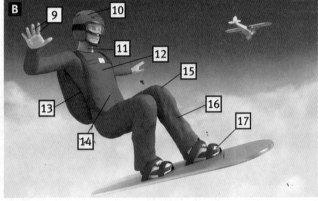

1 h_____	10 h_____
2 h_____	11 n_____
3 a_____	12 c_____
4 s_____	13 b_____
5 e_____	14 s_____
6 f_____	15 k_____
7 e_____	16 l_____
8 m_____	17 f_____
9 f_____	

2 **TRANSLATION** Put the letters in order to make action verbs. Then translate the verbs.

1 thi ___hit_____
2 umjp _____
3 llaf _____
4 ediv _____
5 n´ur _____
6 lyf _____
7 wism _swim_____
8 blicm _____

3 Read the text quickly. Match the sports with the pictures in exercise 1.

Paragraph 1: photo ☑   Paragraph 2: photo ☑

Up in the air!

1 Bungee jumping

Bungee jumping is a popular extreme sport. People jump off tall bridges or buildings on a long elastic rope. They can even jump from helicopters. When the person jumps, the elastic stretches and the jumper flies up very quickly, then down, then up again! It is a very exciting activity, and isn't really dangerous. Lots of people do it, especially on holiday.

2 Sky surfing

Sky surfing is a new extreme sport. Sky surfers jump from planes with a small surfboard on their feet. As the surfers fall, they 'surf' the air and do tricks before they open their parachutes. It's very, very difficult to stand on a surfboard in the air, so there aren't many sky surfers. But there are some sky surfing competitions. The surfers can win medals and prizes. Each surfer needs a cameraman in the air to film the tricks. The films look amazing!

4 Read the text again. Are the sentences true (T) or false (F)?

1 Bungee jumpers sometimes jump from planes. ☐ F
2 Bungee jumping is very dangerous. ☐ F
3 Bungee jumping is a very popular activity. ☐ T
4 Sky surfers jump from buildings and planes. ☐ F
5 Sky surfers wear parachutes. ☐ T
6 Sky surfers compete against one another. ☐

Challenge!

DICTIONARY WORK Find these words in a dictionary and write the translations.

1 elbow _____
2 wrist _____
3 thigh _____
4 calf _____
5 ankle _____
6 eyebrow _____
7 cheek _____
8 chin _____

2F EVERYDAY ENGLISH Expressing likes and dislikes

I can give an opinion about things.

1 Complete the sentences in the chart with the words in the box.

all right awful boring brilliant hate into keen
love not OK on quite really stand terrible think

Good	Quite good	Bad
I _love_ him.	They're _all right_.	She's _awful_.
I _____ he's great.	He's _____ bad.	I can't _____ it.
They're _____.	It's _OK_.	I _____ him.
I'm really _____ them.	I _____ like her.	He's _____.
I'm very keen _____ him.		I'm not very _____ on them.
I _____ like it.		She's _____.

2 Give your opinion of the people and things. Use the verbs and adjectives in the box.

Verbs can't stand hate like love quite like
Adjectives all right awful brilliant great not bad
OK terrible

a Harry Potter films
   I quite like Harry Potter films. They're not bad.

b computer games
   _____

c Beyoncé
   _____

d Robbie Williams
   _____

e classical music
   _____

f Keira Knightley
   _____

3 Match 1–6 with a–f to make questions. Then write true answers.

1 Who's your	☐	a TV programmes do you like?
2 Are you interested	☐	b think of Adele?
3 What's your	☐	c favourite actress?
4 Do you	☐	d in sport?
5 What kind of	☐	e favourite film?
6 What do you	☐	f prefer pop music or rock music?

1 My favourite actress is _____
2 _____
3 _____
4 _____
5 _____
6 _____

4 🎧 LISTENING 14 Listen to Ryan and Julie talking. Are the sentences true (T) or false (F)?

1 Ryan likes football. ☐
2 Ryan watches football on TV, but he doesn't play it. ☐
3 Julie isn't very keen on football. ☐
4 Ryan and Julie both like ice hockey. ☐
5 Julie thinks Al Montoya is awful. ☐
6 Ryan thinks Al Montoya is all right, but he prefers Mark Stuart. ☐

5 🎧 LISTENING 15 Complete the dialogue with the verbs in the box. Then listen and check.

are do isn't like love stand suppose

Frank 1 _Are_ you interested in films?
Carol Yes, I am. I 2 _love_ them.
Frank What's your favourite film?
Carol *The Hobbit.*
Frank Really? It 3 _____ bad, I 4 _____.
Carol So what films 5 _do_ you like, then?
Frank *Transformers* and *X-Men.* They're brilliant films.
Carol Yes, I 6 _____ them too. And I love *Avatar.*
Frank *Avatar?* I can't 7 _____ it.

6 Write a dialogue like the one in exercise 5. Choose a different hobby, sport or interest. Use the ideas in the box or your own ideas.

books football game ice hockey music player
singer/band video games writer

Bev Are you interested in _____ ?
Adam Yes, I am. I love _____ .
Bev _____
Adam _____
Bev Really? _____
Adam _____
Bev _____
Adam _____
Bev _____
Adam _____
Bev _____

Preparation

1 Complete the announcement with the imperatives in the box.

| bring come don't forget join phone visit |

FILM CLUB

Do you like watching films?

Then come and ¹ _join_ our club. We meet every Friday evening at Fran's house at six o'clock.

We watch and talk about our favourite DVDs. We usually bring our own DVDs, but sometimes we rent them.

Every month we meet to decide the next four films.

² _Come_ to our film club! ³ _bring_ a friend!

⁴ _Phone_ Fran on 07784 930324.

⁵ _don't forget_ to tell your friends!

⁶ _Visit_ our website: www.fransfilmclub.org

2 Read the announcement again. Answer the questions.

1 When do they meet? _They meet every Friday evening_

2 Where do they meet? _They meet at Fran's house_

3 What do they do every week? _They watch and talk_
about their favourite DVDs

4 What do they do every month? _Every month they meet_
to decide the next four films

5 Who can you phone? _I can phone Fran_

3 Put the words in order to make imperatives.

1 new / make / friends
Make new friends

2 this / call / number
Call this number

3 club / our / join
Join our club

4 visit / website / our
Visit our website

5 and / do / fit / gymnastics / get
Get fit and do gymnastics

6 favourite / your / hobby / talk about
Talk about your favourite hobby

Challenge!

Complete the imperatives with the verbs below. (They are all instructions from lessons in this unit.)

| Choose Complete Listen Look Use Write |

1 _Complete_ the sentences. _Use_ the present simple.

2 _Choose_ the correct word: adjective or adverb.

3 _Write_ questions about Joe.

4 _Look_ at the table.

5 _Listen_ to the dialogue.

Writing guide

4 Write an announcement for one of the clubs in the box. Follow the writing plan below. Write 50–70 words.

Sports basketball club   cycling club   football club gymnastics club   karate club   tennis club   volleyball club

Other activities art club   athletics club   book club computer club   dance club   jogging club   music club photography club   rollerblading club

1 Give the name of the club.

2 Ask a question.

3 Say when and where it meets.

4 Say what you do at the club.

5 Use an imperative – tell them to come to the club.

6 Give a name and phone number.

7 Tell them to visit your website.

① _____ Club
② Do you like _____?
③ Then join our club. _We meet every_
_Thursday evening at ___ in_
the park.
④ _We read all the new_
books. We...
⑤ _Come to our book club. But..._
⑥ _Phone ___ 1234 5._
⑦ _Visit our website www..._

1 Complete the hobbies and sports. Use *a, e, i, o, u* and *y*.

1 sk _a_ t _e_ b _o_ _a_ rd _i_ ng
2 b _o_ _a_ rd g _a_ m _e_ s
3 _i_ c _e_ h _o_ ck _e_ y
4 _a_ thl _e_ t _i_ cs
5 j _u_ gg _i_ ng
6 f _a_ sh _i_ _o_ n
7 r _o_ ll _e_ rbl _a_ d _i_ ng
8 g _y_ mn _a_ st _i_ cs

Mark: _____ /8

2 Complete the sentences with the correct verb.

1 My sister _____ karate every Friday.
2 I _play_ _____ video games with my brother after school.
3 We sometimes _go_ _____ swimming at weekends.
4 I often _____ to my friends on the phone.
5 Do you _play_ _____ volleyball at school?
6 My dad _watches_ _____ sport on TV every evening.

Mark: _____ /6

3 Rewrite the sentences about Mark's day. Use the adverbs of frequency in brackets.

1 Mark gets up before seven. (sometimes)
   _____

2 He goes to work by bus. (usually)
   _____

3 He's late for work. (never)
   _____

4 He has lunch at home. (hardly ever)
   _____

5 He watches TV in the evening. (always)
   _____

6 He's in bed before midnight. (usually)
   _____

Mark: _____ /6

4 Write questions and answers. Use *can*.

1 Jason / swim?
   _____
   No, _____ .

2 you / use a computer?
   _____
   Yes, _____ .

3 Tom and Anna / drive?
   _____
   Yes, _____ .

4 Mary / speak French?
   _____
   No, _____ .

Mark: ✓ /4

5 Write the adverbs.

1 beautiful _____   4 bad _____
2 hard _____   5 easy _____
3 good _____   6 late _____

Mark: _____ /6

Total: _____ /30

I can ...

Read the statements. Think about your progress and tick one of the boxes.

★ = I need more practice.   ★★ = I sometimes find this difficult.

★★★ = No problem!

	★	★★	★★★
I can talk about my hobbies. (SB p.18)			
I can say how often something happens. (SB p.19)			
I can understand different views on activities. (SB p.20)			
I can say how well I can do something. (SB p.21)			
I can understand an article about extreme sports. (SB p.22)			
I can give an opinion about things. (SB p.24)			
I can write an announcement for a club. (SB p.25)			

PREPARATION: Listening

1 Read the task and the true/false statements carefully.
2 Read the statements again. What do they mean? Write the translations of the words below.
If you do not know, try to guess.
• outdoor event _____
• regularly _____
• race _____
• prize _____
• medal _____
3 Say what you think the listening text is about.

EXAM STRATEGY

• The first time you listen, mark as many statements as you can.
• If you cannot decide if one of the statements is true or false, do not keep thinking about it; listen out for the answers to the other statements.
• The second time you listen, focus on the answers you missed the first time.

EXAM TASK – Listening

🎧 **LISTENING 16** **Listen to an interview with Bob Partridge about an event in Kingsbridge at the weekend. Decide if statements 1–6 are true (T) or false (F).**

1 Bob is talking about an outdoor event. _____
2 The event takes place outside the town. _____
3 The race for runners who practise regularly starts the latest. _____
4 All the races start in the morning. _____
5 There's a special race for very young children. _____
6 There are prizes or medals for everyone who finishes the race. _____

PREPARATION: Reading

1 Read the task and the text. Do not worry if you do not understand every word, just get a general understanding.
2 Answer these questions:
a How many paragraphs are there in the text? _____
b How many headings are there to choose from in the task? _____

EXAM STRATEGY

• Read the first paragraph then read each heading and put a cross by any that are wrong. Decide which heading matches the paragraph.
• Finally, double-check that the extra heading that is left does not match any of the paragraphs.

EXAM TASK – Reading

Read the four advertisements for school clubs. For each advertisement (1–4) choose a suitable heading (A–E). There is one heading you do not need.

1

Do you love board games? Is it difficult to find people to play with you? We are the club for you! Join us every Tuesday evening to think and have fun at the same time. Come and play chess, Scrabble, Cluedo, Trivial Pursuit – any game you want!
Board Games Club, Room 10, every Tuesday, 5 p.m.

2

Calling all girls aged 13–17! Can you move well? Can you sing? Can you learn quickly? Do you want to join our club? We need twenty girls for a new cheerleading group. It's fast! It's fun! It keeps you fit!
Cheerleading Club, Gym, Mondays and Thursdays, 4–6 p.m.

3

Join our new club and discover the amazing things your body can do. We are free runners and we want to teach people how to do it. Come and practise in the park and around the town. Learn to move with speed and style!
Free Running Club, meet at the park on Fridays at 6 p.m.

4

Are you into clothes? Do you have good ideas about fashion? Do you want to design and make your own outfits? We can teach you. Help us organise a fashion show!
Fashion Show Club, Design and Technology Room, Wednesdays, 6–9 p.m.

A Wanted – people with style!
B Move fast! Live free!
C Test your brain – and have fun!
D Come and join the band!
E Jump, wave and shout!

EXAM STRATEGY: Use of English

- If you are not sure which answer is right, try checking which answers are definitely wrong.
- When you have chosen your answers, read the whole text through to check that it makes sense.

EXAM TASK – Use of English

Read the text about Princess Eugenie and complete each gap (1–8) with the correct answer (A–D).

Princess Eugenie [1] _____ a member of the British Royal Family. She's [2] _____ youngest daughter of Prince Andrew and Sarah Ferguson. Her parents [3] _____ married any more. They are divorced. Her older sister's name is Beatrice. Beatrice and Eugenie are Prince William and Harry's cousins. Her grandmother is the Queen and her uncle is Prince Charles. Her full name is Princess Eugenie Victoria Helena of York, so she [4] _____ three first names but no surname.

She studies Art, English and Politics at university in Newcastle. During the holidays she sometimes [5] _____ with her mother and sometimes with her father. She often travels abroad with her parents. Although she's a member of the royal family, she is a normal 20-year-old. She likes going out with her friends, she goes to lots of weddings and parties, and enjoys dancing. She's also really [6] _____ fashion. But because she's a princess, she never has to [7] _____ the housework or cook dinner. She hardly ever has to do any official royal duties but she [8] _____ works for the charities her mother supports.

1 **A** is	**B** are	**C** have	**D** has
2 **A** a	**B** the	**C** an	**D** –
3 **A** aren't	**B** isn't	**C** haven't	**D** hasn't
4 **A** have	**B** is	**C** has	**D** are
5 **A** stays	**B** is staying	**C** stay	**D** stayed
6 **A** keen	**B** prefer	**C** into	**D** like
7 **A** make	**B** makes	**C** do	**D** does
8 **A** always	**B** hardly ever	**C** sometimes	**D** never

PREPARATION: Writing

1 Read the exam task carefully and answer the questions:
   a Who are you going to write to?
   b How long will your email be?
   c How many paragraphs are you going to write?
   d How are you going to begin and end your email?
2 Study the model email text in the Writing Bank on page 110.

EXAM TASK – Writing

Imagine that you would like to find a penfriend in an English-speaking country. You have got the email address of a student from Caerphilly in Wales from your teacher. In your email (100–120 words):

- introduce yourself
- say where you are from
- tell him/her about your family
- tell him/her about your hobbies

PREPARATION: Speaking

1 Work in pairs. Read the exam task. Write down seven questions you could ask to get information about your partner's family, country, hobbies and interests.
2 Now work on your own to invent a new identity for yourself: name, country, age, hobbies and interests, etc.

EXAM STRATEGY: Speaking

- Read the instructions carefully and think who you are going to talk to and what about.
- Think about the key vocabulary that you might use when talking about yourself.
- Talk at length about yourself.
- To express your opinion, use phrases from *Everyday English* in Unit 2.

EXAM TASK – Speaking

STUDENT A:

Think of the new identity you created above. You are on an English course in Britain and want to talk to another student in your group. You would like to know about his/her:

- nationality and country
- family (brothers and sisters)
- hobbies and interests
- favourite sport(s)

Be prepared to answer your new friend's questions too.

STUDENT B:

You are on an English course in Britain. One of the other students in your group is going to ask you some questions about:

- your nationality and country
- your family (brothers and sisters)
- your hobbies and interests
- your favourite sport(s)

Ask your new friend questions to find out some information about him/her too.

3 At school

3A

VOCABULARY AND LISTENING — ## School subjects

I can talk about my school subjects.

1 Complete the opinions with the words in the box.

all great it keen like not quite stand

1 It's _____ .
2 I really _like_ it.
3 It's _____ right.
4 It's _____ bad.
5 I'm not very _keen_ on it.
6 I hate _____ .
7 I can't _____ it.
8 It's _quite_ interesting.

2 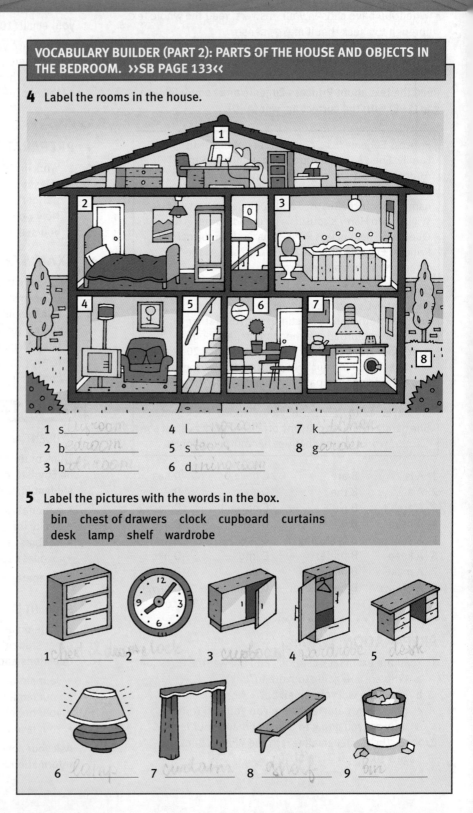 🎧 **LISTENING 17** Listen to Ian and Jill talking. Cross out the incorrect words in the sentences and write the correct words.

1 The next lesson is ~~chemistry~~.
  history

2 Ian doesn't like history.
  loves

3 They never get lots of history homework.
  always

4 Jill likes biology and maths.
  physics

5 Ian is good at physics.
  not very good

6 Their second lesson today is physics.
  history

3 Write about you. Complete the sentences with school subjects.

1 My favourite subjects are _ma___ and _____ .
2 I'm not very keen on _history_ or _science_ .
3 _Phys___ and _____ are all right.
4 I'm good at _____ and _____ .
5 I'm not very good at _____ or _geography_ .

VOCABULARY BUILDER (PART 2): PARTS OF THE HOUSE AND OBJECTS IN THE BEDROOM. ›› SB PAGE 133 ‹‹

4 Label the rooms in the house.

1 s_tudyroom_   4 l_iving room_   7 k_itchen_
2 b_edroom_   5 s_tool_   8 g_arden_
3 b_athroom_   6 d_ining room_

5 Label the pictures with the words in the box.

| bin chest of drawers clock cupboard curtains |
| desk lamp shelf wardrobe |

1 _chest of drawers_   2 _clock_   3 _cupboard_   4 _wardrobe_   5 _desk_

6 _lamp_   7 _curtains_   8 _shelf_   9 _bin_

GRAMMAR *there is / there are; some / any* with plural nouns

I can describe what is in a room and where it is.

1 Choose the correct words.

1 There is / ~~There are~~ a wardrobe in my bedroom.
2 ~~There isn't~~ / There aren't any posters on my bedroom walls.
3 There isn't / ~~There aren't~~ a chest of drawers in my bedroom.
4 There is / ~~There are~~ a dictionary in my bag.
5 ~~There isn't~~ / There aren't any shelves in our classroom.
6 There are / There aren't any curtains in the classroom.
7 There isn't / ~~There aren't~~ a computer on the teacher's desk.

2 Complete the prepositions of place.

1 b_____

2 u_____

3 n_____

4 b_____

5 i_____

6 o_____

7 o_____

8 in f_____ of

3 🎧 **LISTENING 18** Look at the picture and listen to six sentences. Are they true (T) or false (F)?

1	2	3	4	5	6

4 Complete the sentences about the picture in exercise 3. Use *There's a, There isn't a, There are some* or *There aren't any*.

1 _____ computer on the teacher's desk.
2 _____ dictionaries.
3 _____ book on Emily's desk.
4 _____ notice board next to the window.
5 _____ posters.
6 _____ pens on Jack's desk.

5 Write questions and short answers about the picture. Use *Is there a ...* or *Are there any ...* .

1 _Are there any_ _____ chairs?
  Yes, there are.

2 _____ plant near the noticeboard?
_____

3 _____ books on Lottie's desk?
_____

4 _____ posters on the wall?
_____

5 _____ shelves?
_____

6 Look at the picture again and answer the questions. Use prepositions of place.

1 Where's Emily?
  She's between Jack and Lottie.

2 Where's the lamp?
_____

3 Where are the dictionaries?
_____

4 Where's the teacher's chair?
_____

5 Where's the bin?

Challenge!

Write six sentences about your classroom: three with *there is / are* and three with *there isn't / aren't*. Use *a, some,* and *any*.

There's a computer on the teacher's desk.

1 _____
2 _____
3 _____
4 _____
5 _____
6 _____

Revision: Student's Book page 30

1 Complete the sentences with the words in the box.

> canteen   classroom   corridor   gym   hall
> head teacher's office   ICT room   library   music room
> playing field   reception   science lab   stairs
> teachers' room

1 You can find lots of books in the _____ .
2 Visitors to the school go to _____ .
3 You do chemistry in the _____ .
4 You use computers in the _____ .
5 You have lunch in the _____ .
6 You play musical instruments in the _____ .
7 You usually play volleyball and basketball in the
_____ .
8 You play sports like football and hockey on the
_____ .
9 You have lessons in a _____ .
10 At the beginning of the lesson, you wait in the
_____ before you go into the classroom.
11 The teachers meet and talk in the _____ .
12 The whole school can meet in the _____ .
13 You walk up or down the _____ to get to
another floor.
14 The head teacher works in the _____ .

2 Read the text opposite and tick ✓ the true facts. Ignore
gaps 1–4.

The students:
1 only do winter sports. ☐
2 are only from the USA. ☐
3 take normal school exams. ☐
4 sometimes become champions. ☐

3 Match sentences A–E with gaps 1–4 in the text. There is
one sentence that you do not need.

A However, the school stays open in the summer.
B They also do a lot of sport.
C But in the winter the school timetable changes.
D Some students become full-time athletes.
E There are only 120 students and there are only ten
students in a class.

Stratton
Mountain School

Do you love skiing and snowboarding? Do you want
to be an Olympic champion? Then Stratton Mountain
School in Vermont, USA, is the school for you!

It is a small school. ¹___ The students
come from all over the world. They study
hard and do their school exams. ²___

In the summer months, the students can
do athletics, tennis, running, cycling and
skateboarding. ³___ Every morning, the
students go out into the snowy mountains
and train hard. At the moment, there are
68 skiers, 32 snowboarders, 16 cross-country
skiers and four ski jumpers. ⁴___ They
go to the Winter Olympics and World
championships, and many win a medal!

4 🎧 LISTENING 19 Listen to Cindy, a student at Stratton
Mountain School. Complete the sentences with the missing
information.

1 In the winter, Cindy lives at _____ .
2 She shares a _____ with a French girl.
3 In spring, summer and autumn, she lives with
_____ .
4 Breakfast is at _____ o'clock.
5 After the afternoon lessons, she trains for
_____ hours.

Challenge!

Write a description of your school. Write five or six
sentences. Include some of this information:

- number of students and teachers
- sports
- uniform
- number of lessons
- start and finish times
- parts of the school (classrooms, hall, ICT room,
  playing fields, etc.)

There are _____ *students in* _____ .
_____
_____
_____
_____

3D GRAMMAR *have to*

I can talk about something that is necessary or compulsory.

1 Complete the sentences. Use the correct form of *have to* ✓ or *don't have to* ✗.

1 We _____ take exams next summer. ✓
2 I _____ go to the supermarket. ✗
3 My mum _____ work on Saturdays. ✗
4 Kate and Sally _____ study ICT. ✓
5 Dave _____ help his parents at the weekend. ✓
6 You _____ tidy your bedroom. ✗

2 Find the mistakes in the sentences. Write correct sentences.

1 I doesn't have to wear a uniform.
_____

2 Millie doesn't have study French.
_____

3 Have you to arrive at school early?
_____

4 They not have to have lunch at school.
_____

5 We has to work hard at school.
_____

6 Harry don't have to get up early.
_____

3 Complete the text. Use the correct form of *have to* or *don't have to*.

I go to a private school, but it's different from most schools. There's a timetable, but I ¹_____ go to the lessons. Sometimes I play games instead! The teachers usually give us homework, but we ²_____ do it. Every week, we all go to a meeting – the teachers also ³_____ go. At the meeting, we vote to decide the school rules. We all ⁴_____ follow the rules. The head teacher ⁵_____ follow the rules too!

4 Write questions with *have to* and the verbs in the box. Then write true answers.

do	get up	have	help	speak	study	take	wear

1 <u>Do you have to study</u> a foreign language at school?
<u>Yes, we do.</u>

2 _____ with the housework?
_____

3 _____ a school uniform?
_____

4 _____ before 7 a.m. on Mondays?
_____

5 _____ a lot of homework at weekends?
_____

6 _____ lunch at school?
_____

7 _____ an exam at the end of this year?
_____

8 _____ English in English lessons?
_____

5 Order the words to make sentences. Add *have to*.

1 before 9 a.m.? / arrive / you / do / at school
<u>Do you have to arrive at school before 9 a.m.?</u>

2 don't / we / at school / after 3.30 p.m. / stay
_____

3 at school. / we / a lot of sport / do /
_____

4 you / do / chemistry? / study
_____

5 in / we / the school canteen. / eat
_____

6 school? / to / Mandy / the bus / does / take
_____

7 an English test / don't / they / take / week / every
_____

Challenge!

Write five things that you have to do every day.

1 _____
2 _____
3 _____
4 _____
5 _____

Revision: Student's Book page 32

1 Complete the adjectives and choose the correct prepositions.

1 Sally is very g _ _ _ _ **with / at** maths. She always gets excellent marks.

2 I'm b _ _ _ _ _ **in / with** this CD. Can we listen to something else?

3 Jane isn't i _ _ _ _ _ _ _ _ _ _ **in / on** science, but I love it.

4 Harry's exam results are fantastic. His parents are very p _ _ _ _ **of / with** him.

5 Our R.E. teacher sometimes gets a _ _ _ _ _ **on / with** us when we talk in class.

6 Dave isn't very k _ _ _ _ **on / in** French, but he likes German.

2 Read the interview opposite. Match sentences A–F with gaps 1–5. There is one sentence that you do not need.

A We start training after breakfast.

B We don't hit each other.

C We finish training at four o'clock.

D She's a student at the Nakamura Karate School.

E I usually go to a café with the other students.

F Then we have lunch in the school canteen.

3 Choose the correct answers.

1 Olivia comes from **Japan / New Zealand**.

2 Training begins **before / after** breakfast.

3 The students practise fighting in the **morning / afternoon**.

4 Olivia talks to the teachers in **English / Japanese**.

5 In the evenings, the students usually **stay in / go out**.

6 Olivia usually goes to bed **early / late**.

Challenge!

Look at the interview again. Write four questions about the karate school. Use the question words in the box.

how many	what	what time	where

1 _____

2 _____

3 _____

4 _____

Karate School

Olivia White comes from Wellington, New Zealand, but she's in Japan for a month. ¹___

Interviewer	Tell me about the karate school.
Olivia	Well, there are 30 students, and we all come from different countries.
Interviewer	What do you do in a typical day?
Olivia	We have to get up at eight o'clock. ²___
Interviewer	How do you train?
Olivia	In the mornings, we do exercises, but we don't fight. ³___ In the afternoons, we practise fighting.
Interviewer	Is it dangerous?
Olivia	No, not really. ⁴___
Interviewer	How do you understand the teachers? Do they speak English?
Olivia	Yes, they do.
Interviewer	What do you do after training?
Olivia	We go out. ⁵___ But I don't stay out late. We have to be in bed by nine o'clock!

EVERYDAY ENGLISH # Giving directions

I can understand and give directions.

1 Match 1–6 with a–f. Then label the pictures below.

1 Go past ☐ d a the stairs.
2 Go along ☐ b left.
3 Go down ☒ c the corridor.
4 Turn ☐ F d the gym.
5 It's on ☐ e the doors.
6 Go through ☐ f the right.

1 _____

2 _____

3 _____

4 _____

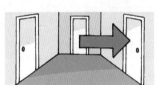

5 _____

6 _____

2 🎧 **LISTENING 20** Look at the plan. Listen to the directions. Start at reception. Where do the people want to go?

1 _____
2 _____
3 _____

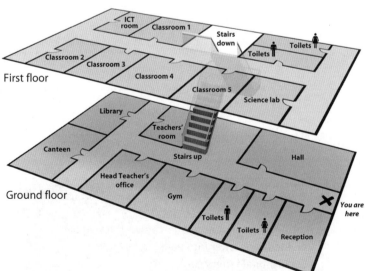

First floor
ICT room | Classroom 1 | Stairs down | Toilets
Classroom 2 | Classroom 3 | Toilets
Classroom 4
Classroom 5 | Science lab

Ground floor
Library | Teachers' room
Canteen | Stairs up | Hall
Head Teacher's office | Gym
Toilets | Toilets | Reception | You are here

3 Put the words in the correct order to make sentences and questions.

a you / please? / repeat / that, / Could

_____

b the / me. / canteen? / Where's / Excuse

_____

c the / the / on / head teacher's office. / It's / right, / opposite

_____

d Where's / I'm / that? / here. / new

_____

4 🎧 **LISTENING 21** Complete the dialogue with the lines in exercise 3. Then listen and check.

Boy ¹___
Girl It's near the library.
Boy Oh, right. ²___
Girl Oh, OK. Go along this corridor and turn left. The canteen is on the right.
Boy ³___ Go along the corridor, turn left …
Girl And ⁴___
Boy Thanks very much.
Girl That's OK.

5 Look again at the plan in exercise 2. Write a dialogue like the one in exercise 4.

A _____ classroom 1?
B It's near _____ room.
A Oh, right. Where's _____ ? I'm _____ .
B _____
_____
_____
A Could _____ ?
_____
B _____
_____
A Thanks _____ .
B _____

Challenge!

Write directions from the entrance of your school to a room.

From the entrance to _____ :

Go _____
_____
_____ .

WRITING **A letter**

I can write a letter to welcome someone to my school.

Preparation

1 **Rewrite the sentences. Add capital letters.**

1 today is wednesday 18th november.
_____

2 fran and tom are from boston in the usa.
_____

3 lawrence and i study german, not italian.
_____

4 we don't study r.e. or ict at my school.
_____

5 my teacher is mr jones. he's from oxford.
_____

6 queen elizabeth lives in buckingham palace.
_____

2 **Complete the letter with the words in the box.**

> Don't forget   I can   I hope you   I look forward
> Most students   There are   Welcome to
> you don't have to   You have to

Dear Heidi,

¹_____ St Mary's Secondary School! I'm your English guide! ²_____ show you around the school and answer your questions. ³_____ enjoy your year here.

⁴_____ be at school before 8.30. Lessons start at 9.00 after assembly. ⁵_____ five lessons in the morning, with a break between 10.15 and 10.35.

Lunch is at 1.00. ⁶_____ buy lunch in the canteen. But ⁷_____ – some students bring sandwiches.

There are three lessons in the afternoon. School finishes at 3.40.

⁸_____ to meeting you.

Bye for now.

Jane

P.S. We have P.E. on Mondays. ⁹_____ your kit!

3 **Complete the information about St Mary's School.**

Arrive at school: _____
Lessons start: _____
Number of lessons in the morning: _____
Break is from: _____ to _____
Lunch is at: _____
Number of lessons in the afternoon: _____
School finishes: _____
P.E. is on: _____

Writing guide

4 **Read the information below about Greenfield School. Write a letter (80–110 words) to a new student. Use the letter in exercise 2 to help you. Follow the plan below, using a new paragraph for each point.**

- Welcome the new student and introduce yourself.
- Write about the morning.
- Write about lunch.
- Write about the afternoon.

Greenfield Secondary School

Arrive at school: before 8.45
Lessons start at: 9.15, after assembly
Number of lessons in the morning: 6
Break is: from 10.45 to 11.05
Lunch is at: 1.15
In the afternoon, lessons start at: 2.10
Number of lessons in the afternoon: 3
School finishes at: 4.30

CHECK YOUR WORK

Have you:
- [ ] included all the information about the school?
- [ ] divided your letter into paragraphs?
- [ ] used capital letters correctly?

1 Write the correct subjects.

1 _____
2 _____
3 _____
4 _____
5 _____
6 _____

Mark: ____ /6

2 Complete the words. Use *a, e, i, o* and *u*. Tick ✓ the parts of a house.

1 k _ tch _ n ☐
2 ch _ st _ f dr _ w _ rs ☐
3 st _ _ rs ☐
4 l _ v _ ng r _ _ m ☐
5 w _ rdr _ b _ ☐
6 n _ t _ c _ b _ _ rd ☐

Mark: ____ /6

3 Write affirmative and negative sentences with *There is, There isn't, There are* or *There aren't*. Use *a, some* or *any*.

1 book on the table ✗
   There isn't a book on the table.

2 clock in my bedroom ✓
   _____

3 shelves in the bathroom ✗
   _____

4 cupboards in the dining room ✓
   _____

5 study in the house ✗
   _____

6 curtains in the living room ✗
   _____

Mark: ____ /5

4 Complete the questions and answers. Use the correct form of *there is / there are* and *a* or *any*.

1 _____ CD player on the desk?
   Yes, _____ .
2 _____ shelves in the classroom?
   No, _____ .
3 _____ pens in the cupboard?
   Yes, _____ .

Mark: ____ /3

5 Label the diagrams with the correct prepositions of place.

1 _____ 2 _____ 3 _____ 4 _____

Mark: ____ /4

6 Complete the sentences. Use the correct form of *have to*: affirmative, negative or interrogative.

1 '_____ you _____ get up early on Saturdays?' 'No, I _____ .'
2 I _____ wear a uniform to school. I can't wear my own clothes.
3 We _____ pay for the tickets. They're free.
4 Sally _____ walk home. She usually takes the bus.
5 '_____ Mark _____ take exams at the end of term?' 'Yes, he _____ .'
6 There's a canteen at Tom's school, but he _____ have lunch there.

Mark: ____ /6

Total: ____ /30

I can ...

Read the statements. Think about your progress and tick one of the boxes.

★ = I need more practice.   ★★ = I sometimes find this difficult.

★★★ = No problem!

	★	★★	★★★
I can talk about my school subjects. (SB p.28)			
I can describe what is in a room and where it is. (SB p.29)			
I can understand information about schools. (SB p.30)			
I can talk about something that is necessary or compulsory. (SB p.31)			
I can understand an interview with a sportsperson. (SB p.32)			
I can understand and give directions. (SB p.34)			
I can write a letter to welcome someone to my school. (SB p.35)			

4 Special occasions

4A   VOCABULARY AND LISTENING   Clothes

I can describe people's clothes.

1 Circle sixteen more items of clothing in the wordsearch.

T	C	H	H	A	T	X	J	E	A	N	S
R	C	B	O	O	T	S	O	E	E	D	V
A	A	U	I	K	R	H	G	M	E	R	L
C	R	U	J	Z	O	O	G	T	S	E	E
K	D	X	D	A	U	E	E	T	C	S	G
S	I	A	P	O	S	S	R	I	A	S	G
U	G	L	O	V	E	S	S	C	R	E	I
I	A	A	D	H	R	Q	U	I	F	S	N
T	N	S	E	C	S	K	I	R	T	O	G
S	W	E	A	T	S	H	I	R	T	C	S
W	J	A	C	K	E	T	S	E	Y	K	S
E	P	I	L	K	S	H	O	R	T	S	O

Rory   Emily   Oliver   Faith

2 🎧 LISTENING 22   Listen to three descriptions. Match them with three of the people in the picture opposite. Write the names.

1 _____   2 _____   3 _____

3 🎧 LISTENING 22   Listen again. Complete the descriptions with clothes from exercise 1.

1 She's got shoes and a black _____ .
  She's got a white _____ and a _____ .

2 She's got black _____ and a black top.
  She's got trainers and white _____ . She's got
  a _____ .

3 He's got jeans and a white _____ . He's got
  _____ and a black _____ .

4 Complete the sentences with true information about your own clothes.

1 I often wear _____
  _____ .

2 I never wear _____
  _____ .

VOCABULARY BUILDER (PART 2): DESCRIBING PEOPLE. ›› SB PAGE 134 ‹‹

5 Complete the questions. Then write true answers.

1 Have you got _glasses_ ?
  _____

2 Have you got c _ _ _ _ _ hair or straight hair?
  _____

3 Have you got l _ _ _ hair or short hair?
  _____

4 Have you got f _ _ _ hair or dark hair?
  _____

5 Have you got a b _ _ _ _ _ or a moustache?
  _____

6 Are you t _ _ _ _ , s _ _ _ _ _ or average height?
  _____

Challenge!

Write a description of the other person in exercise 2. Include clothes from exercise 1 and some of the words in the box.

short / tall	curly / straight	dark / fair	long / short

_____
_____
_____

I can describe things that are happening now.

1 Write the *-ing* form of the verbs.

1 dance _____
2 chat _____
3 read _____
4 smile _____
5 eat _____
6 sing _____
7 run _____
8 cook _____

2 Look at the picture. Complete the sentences with *is* or *are* and your answers from exercise 1.

1 The boy with glasses <u>is</u> <u>eating</u> .
2 The girl with curly hair _____ _____ .
3 The cat and dog _____ _____ .
4 The man with a hat _____ _____ .
5 The woman with long hair _____ _____ .
6 The man with a moustache _____ _____ .
7 The boy and girl on the sofa _____ _____ .
8 The woman with glasses _____ _____ .

3 Complete the sentences. Use the present continuous form of the verbs in the box.

| chat get listen send not sit not use |
| watch not wear |

1 My dad _____ a text message.
2 My cousins _____ to music.
3 Lauren and I _____ TV.
4 Look! Georgia _____ shoes.
5 Wait a minute! I _____ dressed.
6 Mum and Dad _____ the computer.
7 You _____ on your chair.
8 Ben and Leo _____ on the phone.

4 Complete the questions and short answers.

1 <u>Is</u> Emma <u>watching</u> TV? (watch)
  Yes, <u>she is</u> .
2 _____ your uncle _____ French? (speak)
  No, _____ .
3 _____ Adam and Amy _____ basketball? (play)
  Yes, _____ .
4 _____ your parents _____ lunch? (have)
  No, _____ .
5 _____ your dad _____ ? (smile)
  Yes, _____ .
6 _____ you _____ your mum? (help)
  Yes, _____ .

5 Write questions in the present continuous. Then look at the picture and write answers.

1 where / the boy / sit?
  <u>Where is the boy sitting?</u>
  <u>He's sitting on the table.</u>
2 what / the girl / wear?
  _____
  _____
3 what / the boy / eat?
  _____
  _____
4 what / the boy / watch / on TV?
  _____
  _____
5 what / the girl / read?
  _____
  _____

Challenge!

Write three more sentences describing the picture in exercise 5. Use the verbs in the box.

| drink sit wear |

_____
_____
_____

Revision: Student's Book page 40

1 Complete the sentences with the words in the box.

> candles costumes evil graveyard spirit
> supernatural theme

1 The church is next to a _____ .
2 What is the _____ of your fancy dress party?
3 You need _____ for light when there isn't any electricity.
4 We're making our own _____ for the school play.
5 The story is about the fight between good and _____ .
6 Vampires often have _____ powers.
7 He says he often talks to the _____ of his dead father.

2 Look at the photo. Where are the people?

They're in a _____ .

THE DAY OF THE DEAD

The Day of the Dead is an important festival in Mexico. It begins on 31st October and finishes on 2nd November. It is a time to think about friends and family members who are dead. People visit their graves and decorate them with flowers.

According to tradition, the spirits of dead people come back for one day of the year to be with their families. At midnight on 31st October, the spirits of babies and children come. They stay for a day. Then the spirits of the adults come.

Mexican families buy or make sugar skulls for the festival. They often put the name of their dead friend or family member on the skull. They also make a special kind of bread. These days, the festival is changing. Children often wear Halloween costumes, and they sometimes go trick or treating too.

3 Read the text in exercise 2 and choose the correct answers.

1 When does the Day of the Dead festival start?
  a on 31st October
  b on 1st November
  c on 2nd November
2 Why do people say the spirits come back?
  a because it's an important festival
  b because there are flowers on their graves
  c because they want to be with their families
3 Which spirits arrive first?
  a adults and babies
  b babies and children
  c adults
4 What do people often write on the sugar skulls?
  a a name
  b the word 'friend'
  c nothing
5 How is the festival different today from the past?
  a It is not very popular with people now.
  b People bring fruit to the graves now.
  c People follow Halloween traditions now.

4 🎧 LISTENING 23 Listen to a radio programme about festivals and complete the notes. Write one word in each gap.

1 They celebrate 'finados' in Brazil on 2nd _____ .
2 In _____ , they celebrate the Bon Festival in August.
3 The Chinese Ching Ming festival is on 5th _____ .
4 People wear _____ during the Gai Jatra festival in Nepal.
5 The _____ is an important animal at the Gai Jatra festival.

Challenge!

Write about a festival in your country. Include the information below.
- the name of the festival
- when it takes place and how long it lasts
- what people do
- any special food or costumes

_____
_____
_____
_____
_____

1 Match two sentences with each use. Write a, b or c in the boxes.

a an action happening now

b a regular event or action

c a fact which is always true

1 Rebecca has guitar lessons on Fridays. ☐

2 We're feeling excited about the wedding. ☐

3 They speak Portuguese in Brazil. ☐

4 Martha is wearing a beautiful dress. ☐

5 Vegetarians don't eat meat. ☐

6 I usually wear shorts in the summer. ☐

2 Underline the verbs which we do not use in the continuous form.

believe enjoy hate need seem study

3 Complete the email. Use the present simple or continuous form of the verbs in exercise 2.

> ⊠ **Inbox**
>
> Hi Oscar!
>
> How are you? Can I borrow your tennis racquet again? I ¹_____ it for a match on Saturday. My racquet is really old. I ²_____ it.
>
> My sister Gracie is home for the weekend. She ³_____ history at university in Scotland. She ⁴_____ it a lot and she ⁵_____ really happy. She says it's more fun than school and I ⁶_____ her!
>
> Let me know about the racquet!
> Sienna

4 Complete one sentence in each pair with the present continuous and one with the present simple. Use the verb in brackets.

1 (listen)

   a Alisha can't hear you. She _____ to her MP3 player.

   b I _____ to music on the bus every morning.

2 (make)

   a My dad usually _____ dinner at weekends.

   b At school, we _____ a film about the environment.

3 (not speak)

   a I don't understand this part of the film. They _____ English.

   b My parents are from Italy, but I _____ Italian.

4 (not wear)

   a 'I'm cold.'
     'That's because you _____ a jacket.'

   b My mum works for the police, but she _____ a uniform.

5 Read the dialogue. Choose the correct verb forms.

Brooke Hi, Evan. Why ¹**do you wear / are you wearing** that jacket and tie?

Evan ²**I try / I'm trying** it on.

Brooke You usually ³**wear / are wearing** jeans and a sweatshirt.

Evan ⁴**I know / I'm knowing**. But it's my cousin's wedding next month.

Brooke I always ⁵**get / am getting** bored at weddings.

Evan Really? I'm excited about this one. It's in Hollywood.

Brooke ⁶**I don't believe / I'm not believing** you!

Evan It's true. ⁷**I don't joke / I'm not joking**. My cousin ⁸**lives / is living** in California for a year.

6 Look at the pictures and complete the mini-dialogues. Use the present simple or continuous.

Girl 1 Why ¹_____ he _____ (stand) on the table?

Girl 2 He ²_____ (not like) spiders.

Boy Why ³_____ you _____ (not write)?

Girl I ⁴_____ (not understand) the question.

Girl Why ⁵_____ you _____ (laugh)?

Boy I ⁶_____ (watch) a Ben Stiller film.

> **Challenge!**
>
> Write four true sentences about yourself. Write what you (1) are wearing now and (2) are doing now, and what you (3) usually wear and (4) usually do at parties.
>
> 1 _____
> 2 _____
> 3 _____
> 4 _____

I can understand an article about different places.

Revision: Student's Book page 42

1 Complete the puzzle.

[Crossword puzzle with answers filled in: 1 down "bride", 4 across "groom", 6 across "guest"]

1 The _bride_ is a woman on the day of her wedding.

2 The _____ is the part of the wedding when the man and woman get married.

3 The _____ is the party.

4 The _groom_ is a man on the day of his wedding.

5 A _____ is somebody you invite to the wedding.

6 The _____ is the place where the wedding happens.

2 Read the text opposite. Which sentence (a, b or c) is true for all three venues?

a It's inside a famous building.

b It's in London.

c It's part of a hotel.

3 Match sentences 1–6 with venues A–C in the text.

1 There are three different rooms. ☐

2 You can see a famous building from the windows. ☐

3 You can have 200 guests here. ☐

4 It's very cold here. ☐

5 You can see famous people, but they aren't real. ☐

6 This venue is in a museum. ☐

Let's party!

The Icebar, London

The Icebar **A**

Harvey is planning a birthday party for 80 friends, and his venue is really cool – the Icebar in London! Here, it's always -5 °C and everything is made of Swedish ice: the walls, the chairs and the glasses. It's a beautiful and interesting place – but very cold! So there are two other rooms for the guests. These have a Swedish theme too – but they're warm!

Madame Tussauds **B**

Jack is planning a birthday party with twenty stars from the worlds of sport, music and films. But Jack isn't famous – and the stars aren't real. He's planning a party for 60 guests at Madame Tussauds, the famous waxworks museum. Jack says he's really excited about the party because Angelina Jolie is waiting for him there!

The Tower of London **C**

Sue and Olivia are planning a big family party at a famous landmark: the Tower of London. The venue – called the Pavilion – isn't inside the Tower: it's next to it. There's space for 200 guests to have dinner. One wall of the Pavilion has lots of windows, and there are amazing views of the Tower at night.

Challenge!

INTERNET RESEARCH Find another place you can visit in London. Explain what it is (palace? museum? etc.) and what you can do there.

_____

_____

_____

_____

_____

Making arrangements

I can make arrangements to meet somebody.

1 What plans do Julia and Reece have for the weekend? Look at the chart. Then write sentences using the present continuous.

	Julia	Reece
Saturday a.m.	play football	play football
p.m.	watch TV	go shopping
Sunday a.m.	do homework	do homework
p.m.	visit friends	have a barbecue

1 Julia and Reece _are playing football_ on Saturday morning.
2 Julia _is watching TV_ on Saturday afternoon.
3 Reece _is going shopping_ on Saturday afternoon.
4 Julia and Reece _are doing homework_ on Sunday morning.
5 Julia _is visiting friends_ on Sunday afternoon.
6 Reece _is having a barbecue_ on Sunday afternoon.

2 🎧 LISTENING 24 Complete the dialogue with the missing lines. Then listen and check.

> Are you free in the afternoon?
> I can't skate!
> See you then!
> What are your plans for Sunday?
> What time?

Leon Hi, Amber. ¹ _What are your plans for Sunday_
Amber I'm meeting friends in the morning.
Leon ² _Are you free in the afternoon?_
Amber Yes, I am.
Leon How about going ice skating?
Amber No, thanks. ³ _I can't skate._
Leon Oh, OK. Well, shall we go to the park?
Amber Yes, OK. ⁴ _What time?_
Leon Let's meet in the park at three o'clock.
Amber Fine. ⁵ _See you then!_

3 Complete the chart of activities with the verbs in the box.

go   have   meet   play

1 _have_	dinner in a café / lunch in a café
2 _play_	volleyball / video games
3 _meet_	friends
4 _go_	dancing / ice skating / skateboarding / to the beach

4 Write true answers.

1 What are you doing this evening?
I am doing the homework this evening.

2 What are you doing on Sunday afternoon?
I'm watching movie on Sunday afternoon.

5 Write *in*, *on* or *at*. Put a tick ✓ if the expressions are correct without a preposition.

1 _____ tomorrow ✓
2 _at_ three o'clock
3 _in_ the weekend
4 _in_ the afternoon
5 _at_ night
6 _____ tomorrow evening ✓
7 _on_ Monday morning
8 _____ this evening ✓
9 _on_ Sunday

6 Match 1–8 with a–h.

1 That — d
2 What are your — h
3 Shall we — c
4 What are you — a
5 How about — g
6 Are you free — e
7 That's — b
8 I'm afraid — d

a up to tonight?
b perfect.
c go to the park?
d I can't.
e this weekend?
f sounds fun.
g playing football?
h plans for Saturday?

7 Write a dialogue like the one in exercise 2. Use activities from exercise 3.

Eve Hi Alan. What are your plans for Saturday?
Alan I'm meeting friends in the morning.
Eve Are you free in the afternoon?
Alan Yes I am.
Eve How about going to the beach?
Alan No, thanks. I can't go to the beach.
Eve Oh, okay. Shall we have dinner in a café?
Alan Sounds great. What time?
Eve Let's meet at the cafe at five o'clock.
Alan That's perfect. See you then.

Preparation

1 Complete the invitations with the expressions in the box.

> Hi   Hope you can come.   I'm having a party
> Love   Please let me know.

Dear Millie
It's my birthday! ¹_____ on Saturday 12ᵗʰ May at my house. It starts at 8.30 p.m. and it finishes late! It's a fancy dress party and the theme is Hollywood. Can you bring some music?
²_____ Please reply by text or email.
³_____

Gracie

⁴_____ Bradley
I'm having a barbecue to celebrate the end of our exams. It's on Friday 16ᵗʰ June at the Village Hall. It starts at four o'clock in the afternoon. Can you bring some burgers?
Hope you can make it. ⁵_____
Bye for now
Blake

2 Complete the chart with information from the invitations in exercise 1.

	Gracie's party	Blake's party
Day and date	Sat 12ᵗʰ May	
Start time		4. .
Venue		Village Hall
Special occasion		
What to bring		burgers

3 Match 1–4 with a–d. Then write them as requests with *can*. Include *please* at the end.

1 Invite your   a phone.
2 Reply by   b food and drink.
3 Wear   c sister.
4 Bring some   d fancy dress.

1 Can you invite your sister, please?
2 _____
3 _____
4 _____

Writing guide

4 Complete the message with the abbreviations in the box.

> etc.   e.g.   St

Hi Harry
It's my birthday next Saturday and I'm meeting some school friends (Mick, Ian, ¹_____) in town. Can you come? We're going to the new restaurant in Lake ²_____ . The food is great and you can have two dishes (³_____ a pizza and a salad) for £5!

5 Imagine you are having a party. Complete the chart with information about it.

	Your party
Day and date	
Start time	
Venue	
Special occasion	
What to bring	

6 Write an invitation to a party. Follow steps 1–6 below. Write 40–60 words.

1 Greet your friend with *Dear…* or *Hi…* .
2 Say what type of party you are having.
3 Say the time and day / date.
4 Say the place.
5 Make a request with *Can you … ?*
6 End the invitation.

_____
_____
_____
_____
_____

CHECK YOUR WORK

Have you:
- [ ] written 40–60 words?
- [ ] started and finished your invitation with suitable phrases?
- [ ] included all the information in the task in exercise 6?
- [ ] checked your spelling and grammar?

1 Label the pictures with eight of the words in the box.

| boots | cardigan | dress | gloves | jacket | leggings |
| scarf | shirt | shorts | skirt | socks | trainers | trousers |

1 _____
2 _____
3 _____
4 _____
5 _____
6 _____
7 _____
8 _____

Mark: ___ /8

2 Look at the picture. Choose the correct words.

1 The man is **tall / short**.
2 The woman has got **a beard / glasses**.
3 The man has got **glasses / a moustache**.
4 The boy has got **dark / fair** hair.
5 The boy has got **curly / straight** hair.
6 The girl has got **dark / fair** hair.

Mark: ___ /6

3 Complete the sentences. Use the present continuous affirmative ✓ or negative ✗ form of the verbs in brackets.

1 Harriet _____ breakfast. (have ✓)
2 My parents _____ TV. (watch ✗)
3 John _____ on the phone. (chat ✓)
4 My cousins _____ basketball. (play ✓)
5 Ella _____ with Louis. (dance ✗)
6 Dad and I _____ dinner. (make ✗)

Mark: ___ /6

4 Read the answers and complete the questions. Use a question word from the box and the present continuous.

| what | where | who | why |

1 '_____ (we / meet) in town?' 'My sister.'
2 '_____ (you / have) for breakfast?' 'Cereal.'
3 '_____ (we / play) tennis?' 'At the park.'
4 '_____ (he / wear) a tie?' 'He's going to work.'

Mark: ___ /4

5 Complete the dialogue. Use the present simple or present continuous form of the verbs in brackets.

Zara Hi, Joe. What ¹_____ you _____ (do)?

Joe I ²_____ (play) my new video game. ³_____ you _____ (want) to play?

Zara No, thanks. I ⁴_____ (not like) video games. Let's go to the park. Look! The sun ⁵_____ (shine). It's a beautiful day.

Joe I can't stop my game now, I ⁶_____ (win)!

Mark: ___ /6

Total: ___ /30

I can ...

Read the statements. Think about your progress and tick one of the boxes.

★ = I need more practice.   ★★ = I sometimes find this difficult.

★★★ = No problem!

	★	★★	★★★
I can describe people's clothes. (SB p.38)			
I can describe things that are happening now. (SB p.39)			
I can understand information about a festival. (SB p.40)			
I can talk about what usually happens and what is happening now. (SB p.41)			
I can understand an article about different places. (SB p.42)			
I can make arrangements to meet somebody. (SB p.44)			
I can write an invitation to a party. (SB p.45)			

PREPARATION: Reading

Read the task instructions and the questions with multiple-choice answer options. What general information does it give you about the topic?

EXAM STRATEGY

- Read the text for general understanding.
- Now read the first statement and options A–C. Find the part of the text that contains the answer. Then cross out any options that are clearly wrong.
- Decide which option is correct. If you cannot decide between two options, make an intelligent guess.
- Repeat the process for the remaining statements and options.

EXAM TASK – Reading

Read the article about an unusual student in Kenya. Choose the correct answer (A–C) for each question (1–5).

An unusual student

There is an unusual student in Class One of Kapkendulywa Primary School in Kenya. Kimani Maruge is Class One's star pupil. But he is a bit different from his classmates. Kimani Maruge is 85 years old. He wears a hearing aid and uses a stick to walk. But every morning he arrives at the school and sits down in the classroom.

'I can't read or write, and now this is my chance to learn,' Kimani says. 'For the first time there is free education in Kenya. It is very important to me. A person is never too old to learn.'

Jane Obinchu, the head teacher of the primary school, agrees with her new pupil. 'I think it is a good idea,' she says.

Kimani has to do the same as all the other students in the class. He has to sit at the same desk and wear the same uniform – a white shirt, blue shorts and a blue jumper. He is a very good student. He works very hard in class. Kimani's teacher, Ezric Muniu, says, 'Kimani is so clever. Now he reads the newspapers.'

Joseph and Charles are Kimani's classmates. They are both eight years old. Joseph says, 'Now he is our friend. He teaches us songs and tells us stories about the old times.' Charles agrees. 'My grandparents live very far from here, so it is good that we can have Guga.' Kimani's nickname in class is Guga. It means 'grandad'.

Education in Kenya is now free and for everyone. But there aren't enough schools. In Kapkendulywa Primary School there are now 890 students – that's 100 pupils in each class! 'But we are happy that so many children have a chance to learn,' says Mrs Obinchu.

1 Kimani Maruge is an unusual student because he
   A is older than the other students.
   B is a very good student.
   C cannot hear very well.
2 Kimani Maruge goes to school because he
   A wants to become a teacher.
   B has a lot of free time.
   C doesn't have to pay for it.
3 In the classroom, Kimani Maruge
   A doesn't do much work.
   B wears special clothes for school.
   C reads newspapers.
4 Kimani Maruge's classmates
   A don't accept him because he's too old.
   B laugh at him.
   C like him very much.
5 In Kenya
   A there are many good schools.
   B only rich people can go to school.
   C there are a lot of pupils in classes.

PREPARATION: Listening

1 Read the exam task carefully. Brainstorm words that the speakers may use.
2 The first time you listen, try to identify key words and expressions.

EXAM STRATEGY

The first time you listen, take notes about what each speaker is saying. The second time, choose the right answers.

EXAM TASK – Listening

🎧 LISTENING 25 Listen to five young people talking about a special event in their lives. Match each question (A–F) to one of the speakers (1–5). There is one question you do not need.

Which speaker is talking about:

A a sports event? _____
B clothes they don't like wearing? _____
C their wedding? _____
D an important birthday party? _____
E a new family member? _____
F a music event? _____

PREPARATION: Use of English

1 Complete these sentences. What is the difference?
   a Jack _____ tennis every day.
   b Jack _____ tennis right now.

EXAM STRATEGY

- Read the whole sentence before you choose the answer.
- To make sure your answer is right, check whether it matches the grammar (singular or plural, correct person, etc.) and makes sense.

EXAM TASK – Use of English

Choose the correct alternatives.

Barry Comprehensive School is a secondary school in a small town in South Wales. It's only forty-five years old. [1]*There are / There is* about 1,500 students, but they don't live at the school – they live at home. They start school when they are eleven and leave when they are sixteen or eighteen. There aren't [2]*some / any* girls in Years 7–11 but there are some girls in Year 12. There's a girls' school in the town as well.

The school is a comprehensive and it's free for students. Most students [3]*live / lives* in the town or in the local villages. Students either walk to school or come by bus. The boys start school at 8.50 and they [4]*don't have to / have to* wear a uniform: a green sweatshirt and black trousers.

Sport is very important at Barry Comprehensive. There are rugby, cricket, basketball and football teams that play against [5]*some / any* of the other local schools.

Gethin [6]*is going / goes* to Barry Comprehensive School, he [7]*is studying / studies* for his A-levels. Because he's in Year 12, he [8]*doesn't have to / has to* wear a uniform. Today he's wearing jeans and a T-shirt. His best friend Cai is not in school today. This morning he [9]*is doing / does* work experience at the local newspaper.

PREPARATION: Writing

Read the exam task below and answer the questions.
a What type of text are you going to write?
b Who is it for?
c What is it about?
d Do you need to use formal or informal language?

EXAM STRATEGY

- Think about who is going to read your letter.
- Read the task instructions carefully and think about how many pieces of information you have to include.
- Organise your letter. Think about which ideas you are going to write about in each paragraph.
- Make sure that you have covered all the points in the task.
- When you have finished, check your work carefully for mistakes in grammar, spelling or vocabulary.

EXAM TASK – Writing

In a letter to a friend from Scotland, describe a special event that you celebrate with your family. Write 160–180 words. In your letter:

- say what the event is and when it takes place
- write how your family celebrates and what you usually do
- explain what you think of the event and why
- ask your friend about a special event in his/her country and invite him/her to your own country

PREPARATION: Speaking

1 Before you begin to describe the picture, think about your answers to these questions:
   a Who is in the picture?   c What are they doing?
   b Where are the people?   d How are they feeling?
2 Look at the expressions in the last exam strategy below. Work in pairs. Take turns to read an expression and point to the correct part of one of the pictures.

EXAM STRATEGY

- Describe the situation and express your opinion.
- Use the present continuous to describe what the people are doing. When you express your opinion or describe the place, use the present simple.
- Use *in the picture, on the right/left, in the middle/background/foreground, at the top/at the bottom.*

EXAM TASK – Speaking

Work in pairs. Choose one of the pictures and describe it to your partner. He/She should guess which picture you are describing. Then tell your partner how you think the students are feeling. Do you enjoy school? Why / Why not?

When you have finished, change roles and do the task again.

5 Healthy living

I can talk about different foods and dishes.

1 Do the word puzzle. What are the hidden food words?

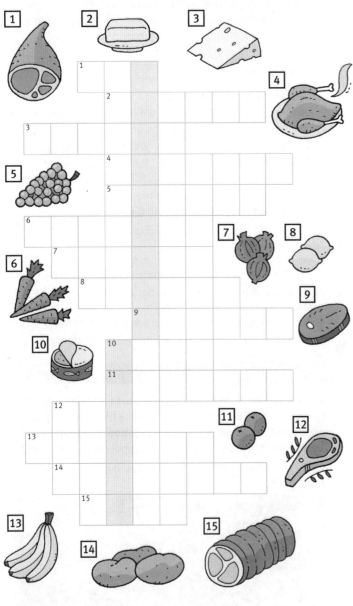

The hidden words are _____ and _____ .

2 Match food categories 1–4 with example foods a–d. Then add one more food to each category.

1 fish and seafood	a	butter, _____
2 meat	b	carrots, _____
3 dairy products	c	salmon, _____
4 fruit and vegetables	d	beef, _____

3 Look at the picture and complete the description below.

This person is having a ¹b_____ of rice with prawns, two ²s_____ of cheese, a small ³b_____ of grapes and a ⁴g_____ of water.

4 🎧 **LISTENING 26** Listen to five people talking about their likes and dislikes. Tick ✓ the speaker who would like the food in exercise 3.

Speaker:	1	2	3	4	5	

VOCABULARY BUILDER (PART 2): METHODS OF COOKING. >>SB PAGE 135<<

5 What are the people cooking? Label the pictures with an adjective from box A and a type of food from box B.

 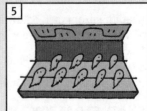

A
baked ~~boiled~~ fried grilled roast

B
~~carrots~~ chicken eggs potatoes prawns

1 _boiled carrots_
2 _____
3 _____
4 _____
5 _____

5B GRAMMAR Quantity

I can talk about quantities.

1 Are these nouns usually countable or uncountable? Write C (countable) or U (uncountable).

1 beef	U	6 salt	☐	11 fruit	☐
2 apple	C	7 tomato	☐	12 bread	☐
3 ham	☐	8 potato	☐	13 vegetable	☐
4 grape	☐	9 sugar	☐	14 pork	☐
5 water	☐	10 sandwich	☐	15 tuna	☐

2 Write the plural form of the countable nouns in exercise 1. Add *-s* or *-es*.

apples _____ _____

_____ _____ _____

3 Complete the sentences and questions with *some* and *any*.

1 Have we got _____ milk?

2 There isn't _____ sugar in this coffee.

3 There are _____ apples in the bowl.

4 Is there _____ ham in the fridge?

5 There's _____ meat on your plate.

6 Is there _____ butter in this sandwich?

7 There are _____ prawns on this pizza.

8 Are there _____ carrots in the bag?

4 What's on the table? Write sentences. Use *There's some* (+ uncountable noun) or *There are some* (+ plural noun).

1 (bread) There's some bread.

2 (ham) _____

3 (sandwiches) _____

4 (grapes) _____

5 (apples) _____

6 (tomatoes) _____

7 (milk) _____

8 (sugar) _____

5 🎧 LISTENING 27 Complete the dialogue with *How much* or *How many*. Then listen and check.

Louis OK. Let's make this pizza. [1] How much _____ oil do we need?

Karen We need half a cup of oil.

Louis OK. What else? [2] _____ flour do we need?

Karen 300 grams.

Louis And [3] _____ cheese?

Karen 200 grams. We also need tomatoes, peppers and ham.

Louis OK. [4] _____ tomatoes do we need?

Karen We need four.

Louis Good. Here they are. [5] _____ peppers?

Karen Two red ones.

Louis OK. And finally, [6] _____ ham do we need?

Karen Three slices.

Louis Great! We've got everything we need.

Challenge!

Write the questions. Use *How much* or *How many*. Then write true answers.

1 books / read / a year?

_____

_____

2 housework / do / a week?

_____

_____

3 exams / have / a month?

_____

_____

4 coffee / drink / a day?

_____

_____

5C   CULTURE   Unusual diets

I can understand information about different diets.

Revision: Student's Book page 50

1 Match 1–6 with a–f to make compound nouns.

1	processed	☐	a	food
2	farm	☐	b	products
3	balanced	☐	c	animals
4	animal	☐	d	body
5	human	☐	e	products
6	dairy	☐	f	diet

2 Complete the sentences with the compound nouns from exercise 1.

1 Honey and eggs are _____ .

2 A _____ is important for your health.

3 The _____ needs food and water.

4 Some _____ , like cheese and butter, are fattening.

5 I don't eat _____ , like burgers or salami.

6 _____ need a lot of food and water.

3 Read the text opposite. What is the 'caveman diet' about? Choose a, b or c.

a what to eat

b what to eat and how often to eat

c what to eat, how often to eat, and how to eat

4 Read the text again. Are the sentences true (T) or false (F)?

1 We eat a lot of wheat today because it's good for our health. ☐

2 People choose the caveman diet because they don't like meat. ☐

3 People on the caveman diet don't eat bread because it's a modern food. ☐

4 On the caveman diet you can eat fish, but not fruit. ☐

5 The caveman diet tells you what to eat and how to eat. ☐

6 People on the cavemen diet have six large meals a day. ☐

5 🎧 **LISTENING 28** Listen to four people talking about what they eat. Match sentences A–E with speakers 1–4. There is one sentence that you do not need.

A This speaker is a vegetarian, but not a vegan.

B This speaker is a vegan.

C This speaker doesn't eat any fruit.

D This speaker is not a vegetarian or a vegan and isn't on the caveman diet.

E This speaker is on the caveman diet.

Speaker:

1	2	3	4

Caveman power!

In the modern world, our food comes from farms. We eat a lot of rice and wheat (in pasta, bread, etc.) because it's easy to grow. And from farm animals, we get meat and dairy products. But some people believe that this modern diet is not good for the human body: they prefer a 'caveman diet', from the days before farms.

People who follow the caveman diet don't eat 'modern' things like bread, processed food, potatoes and dairy products. So what can they eat? Well, nuts, seeds and fruit are OK. A lot of vegetables are OK too. And they can eat meat and fish.

But the caveman diet is not just about the type of food – it's also about the way you eat it. Forget breakfast, lunch and dinner – you now have six small meals a day. And you eat them with your hands!

Challenge!

Write six different kinds of food you can eat on the caveman diet. Don't write the foods in the text again.

_____

_____

_____

5D GRAMMAR *should / shouldn't*

I can give advice.

1 Complete the sentences with *should* or *shouldn't* and the verbs in the box.

drink	~~eat~~	eat	go	play	read	watch	wear

1 I _shouldn't eat_ these chips. I'm not hungry.
2 He _____ this book. It's great!
3 We _____ home now. Mum's making dinner for us.
4 You _____ coffee now – it's time for bed!
5 They _____ football outside. It's a beautiful day.
6 You _____ a coat. It's very cold.
7 She _____ the bread. It's old.
8 You _____ TV all evening. You've got homework!

2 Read the sentences. Then write advice. Use *should* or *shouldn't* and the words in brackets.

1 That car looks dangerous.
   (we / go near it)
   We shouldn't go near it.

2 My brother wants to earn some money.
   (he / get a part-time job)
   _____

3 These prawns don't taste very good.
   (we / eat them)
   _____

4 I'm not feeling well.
   (I / go to bed)
   _____

5 The nightclub is for adults, and the boys are only fourteen.
   (they / go inside)
   _____

6 I don't like raw carrots.
   (we / cook them)
   _____

7 It's her dad's birthday tomorrow.
   (she / buy him a present)
   _____

3 Look at the pictures. Write questions with *Should he / she / they …?* and the prompts. Then write your own answers.

1 eat the fish?
   Should she eat the fish?
   Yes, she should. /
   No, she shouldn't.

2 go outside?
   _____
   _____

3 go to bed?
   _____
   _____
   _____

4 buy the computer?
   _____
   _____
   _____

5 see the film?
   _____
   _____
   _____

Challenge!

How many different questions and answers can you write for this picture? Use the verbs in the box or your own ideas.

climb	fight	hide
run	shout	

_____
_____

_____
_____
_____
_____
_____

I can understand an article about different health treatments.

Revision: Student's Book page 52

1 Complete the dialogue with the words in the box.

> cure   headache   medicine   painful   patients
> relax   treatment

Ari   Hi! How are you?

Jade Not great. I've got a bad ¹_____ at the moment. It's really ²_____ . And I'm so busy!

Ari   Oh dear. You need to sit down and ³_____ . Perhaps try a natural ⁴_____ , like a massage.

Jade Massage? No, I need some ⁵_____ from the doctor.

Ari   Doctors can't ⁶_____ everything, you know. And they never talk to their ⁷_____ .

Jade I don't want a conversation. I want to feel well!

2 Look quickly at the text opposite. What is it about?

a Three cures for skin problems.

b Therapies that use food or drink.

c Three unusual kinds of therapy.

3 Choose the best answers.

1 In a hay bath, there's
   a hay, water, flowers and plants.
   b only hay and water.
   c only hay.

2 One problem with hay baths is
   a they sometimes give you a headache.
   b you often get very cold.
   c they aren't always comfortable.

3 An ice sauna is
   a very warm.
   b very cold.
   c hot and then cold.

4 The view from an ice sauna is beautiful because
   a ice is beautiful.
   b you can see through the walls.
   c you can see other people.

5 In what order are the four parts of the beer bath treatment?
   a Beer bath, sleep, shower, swim.
   b Shower, beer bath, swim, sleep.
   c Beer bath, shower, sleep, swim.

6 How much does the beer bath cost at Hedwig Bauer's hotel?
   a 20 euros.   b 30 euros.   c 44 euros.

Relax!

Hay bath

Hay baths are a very old treatment from the mountains in the north of Italy. It's a very simple idea. Patients take off their clothes and lie in wet hay. There are flowers and plants in the hay too. It gets very hot, so it isn't always comfortable, but some people believe it is very good for your health and can cure headaches.

Ice sauna

Saunas are very hot places – ice is very cold. So can you build a sauna out of ice? The answer is yes! They do it in Russia and Finland during the long winters. A fire makes the sauna very warm inside: over 60°C! And because the walls are ice, you have a beautiful view of the world outside.

Beer bath

Beer baths are a popular treatment in the Czech Republic and Austria. Hedwig Bauer has a hotel in Austria where you can have a 30-minute beer bath for 44 euros. After the bath, patients sleep for 20 minutes. Then they have a shower and go swimming. 'Beer is very good for the skin,' says Hedwig.

Challenge!

Imagine you can have one of the three therapies in the text. Decide which therapy and give a reason.

I like the idea of the _____ because

_____

_____ .

1 Complete the dishes (1–7) on the menu with the words in the box.

chips   coffee   curry   garlic   juice   sandwich   stir

Kirsty's Café
MEALS

Mushroom soup with ¹_____ bread   a _____

Vegetable ²_____ with rice   £6.50

Chicken and ham pie with vegetables   b _____

Mushroom omelette with ³_____   £4.75

Beef ⁴_____-fry with noodles   £5.95

Salmon salad   c _____

Toasted cheese and ham ⁵_____   £2.75

DRINKS

Fruit ⁶_____   £1.60

Banana milkshake   d _____

⁷_____ or tea   £1.80

2 🎧 **LISTENING 29** Now listen and write the missing prices (a–d) in the menu.

3 Put the words in the correct order to make sentences and questions.

a juice / I'd / orange / like / an

_____

b curry, / can / have / please / I / the / ?

_____

c help / I / you / can / ?

_____

d are / you / here

_____

e drink / to / anything / ?

_____

4 Complete gaps 1–5 of the dialogue with lines a–e from exercise 3. Then write the correct price for the total.

Woman Hello. ¹___

Ryan Yes. Let me see … ²___

Woman Yes, certainly. ³___

Ryan Yes, please. ⁴___ .

Woman So, vegetable curry and an orange juice.
⁵___ . Is that all?

Ryan Yes, it is.

Woman Great. That's ⁶£_____ , please.

Ryan Thank you.

5 🎧 **LISTENING 30** Listen and check.

6 Rewrite the sentences using *would like* instead of *want*.

1 Do you want some bread?
   Would you like some bread?

2 My friend wants a sandwich.

_____

3 We want some more coffee.

_____

4 Does your dad want some cake?

_____

5 I want to go home now.

_____

6 My mum wants sugar in her tea.

_____

7 Do you want to go out for dinner?

_____

7 Write a dialogue like the one in exercise 4. Choose different food and drink from the menu in exercise 1.

Kirsty _____

Nicole _____

_____

Kirsty _____

Nicole _____

Kirsty _____

_____

Nicole _____

Kirsty _____

Nicole _____

I can write a questionnaire about food and lifestyle.

Preparation

1 Choose the correct words in these questions about food.

1 **How / What** healthy is your diet?

2 **Are / Do** you a vegetarian?

3 **How / When** often do you eat chips?

4 **Are / Do** you always have breakfast?

5 **When / What** do you usually have for breakfast?

6 **Does / Is** your diet include fruit and vegetables?

2 Match the questions in exercise 1 with answers a–f.

a No, I'm not. ☐

b About three times a week. ☐

c Fruit, bread and butter. ☐

d It's quite healthy, in my opinion. ☐

e Yes, it does. ☐

f Yes, I do. ☐

3 Write your own answers to the questions in exercise 1.

1 _____

2 _____

3 _____

4 _____

5 _____

6 _____

4 Find the mistake in each question. Rewrite the questions correctly.

1 How much burgers do you eat a week? ✗

   How many burgers do you eat a week?

2 Do you eat ever chocolate? ✗

   _____

3 What usually have you for lunch? ✗

   _____

4 How much water you drink every day? ✗

   _____

5 Do you be a vegetarian? ✗

   _____

6 How fish do you eat a week? ✗

   _____

5 **TRANSLATION** Translate the questions.

1 How do you relax?

   _____

2 How much exercise do you do a week?

   _____

3 What time do you usually go to bed?

   _____

4 Do you enjoy sport?

   _____

5 Are you a member of a gym?

   _____

6 Do you walk to school?

   _____

Writing guide

6 Write a questionnaire with three questions about food and three questions about lifestyle. Use questions from exercises 4 and 5 or your own ideas.

Health questionnaire: food and lifestyle
1 _____ _____
2 _____ _____
3 _____ _____
4 _____ _____
5 _____ _____
6 _____ _____

CHECK YOUR WORK

Have you:

☐ formed your questions correctly?

☐ included three questions on each topic?

☐ checked your spelling?

7 Ask a friend or family member the questions in exercise 6 (in your own language, if necessary). Translate their answers into English and write them in the questionnaire.

1 Label the food pictures with the words in the box.

| butter   chicken   eggs   peas   potato   rice   salmon |

1 _____ 2 _____ 3 _____ 4 _____ 5 _____ 6 _____ 7 _____

Mark: ___ /7

2 Choose the correct words to describe the food in exercise 1.

1 The potato is **baked** / **fried**.
2 The salmon is **boiled** / **grilled**.
3 The eggs are **boiled** / **fried**.
4 The chicken is **fried** / **roasted**.

Mark: ___ /4

3 Underline the uncountable noun in each group. (Remember, an uncountable noun has no plural form.)

1 banana   egg   prawn   tuna
2 carrot   grape   pork   tomato
3 apple   beef   lemon   mushroom
4 butter   orange   sandwich   vegetable

Mark: ___ /4

4 Complete the questions with *How much* or *How many*.

1 _____ people are in your address book?
2 _____ lessons has she got this morning?
3 _____ money have we got?
4 _____ food does your dog eat?
5 _____ brothers have you got?

Mark: ___ /5

5 Complete the sentences. Use *should* or *shouldn't* and verbs in the box.

| ask   eat   read   ride   use   work |

1 You _____ hard. You've got exams this week.
2 I _____ my sister. She usually knows the answer.
3 We _____ this computer. It isn't ours.
4 He _____ his bike in the shopping centre. It's dangerous.
5 You _____ my email. It's funny!
6 I _____ chips every day. They aren't good for my health.

Mark: ___ /6

6 Complete the questions. Use a question word from the box, the words in brackets, and *should*.

| how   what   when   where |

1 _____ (she / send) the invitations?
Next week.
2 _____ (I / cook) the fish?
With butter and lemon.
3 _____ (we / put) the eggs?
In the fridge.
4 _____ (they / wear) for the wedding?
Smart clothes.

Mark: ___ /4

Total: ___ /30

I can ...

Read the statements. Think about your progress and tick one of the boxes.

★ = I need more practice.   ★★ = I sometimes find this difficult.

★★★ = No problem!

	★	★★	★★★
I can talk about different foods and dishes. (SB p.48)			
I can talk about quantities. (SB p.49)			
I can understand information about different diets. (SB p.50)			
I can give advice. (SB p.51)			
I can understand an article about different health treatments. (SB p.52)			
I can order food and drink in a café. (SB p.54)			
I can write a questionnaire about food and lifestyle. (SB p.55)			

6A VOCABULARY AND LISTENING In town

I can describe places in a town.

1 Complete the places with the words in the box.

bus cinema church concert hall information office leisure library shopping station theatre train

1 _____
2 _____ hall
3 _____ stop
4 _____
5 _____
6 _____
7 _____
8 police _____
9 _____ centre
10 town _____
11 _____ station
12 _____ centre

2 🎧 LISTENING 31 Listen and complete the directions.

1 Go _____ on, take the second _____ and go past the _____ . The library is on the left _____ the train station.

2 Take the _____ left and the _____ is on the left, _____ the bank.

3 Yes, go straight on, _____ the first right, go _____ the leisure centre and the theatre is on the _____ .

3 Read the directions in exercise 2 again. Then look at the routes on the map and identify places 1–7.

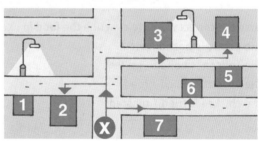

1 _____   5 _____
2 _____   6 _____
3 _____   7 _____
4 _____

VOCABULARY BUILDER (PART 2): COLLOCATIONS. >>SB PAGE 136<<

4 Complete the phrases with the words in the box.

a car   to a friend   a pizza   to a night club   a train
go   leave   send   visit   watch

1 catch _____   6 _____ a letter
2 _____ for a walk   7 go _____
3 park _____   8 _____ a message
4 _____ a museum   9 chat _____
5 order _____   10 _____ a film

5 Find eight more incorrect prepositions. Write the correct prepositions.

1 I usually go ~~in~~ bed after midnight. _to_
2 This evening I'm staying at home. ✓
3 James is listening at music. _____
4 We live on a small house. _____
5 What do you usually have in breakfast? _____
6 My sister studies maths at university. _____
7 Marc and Chantal are of France. _____
8 My dad drives in work in the morning. _____
9 Our maths teacher gives us a lot of homework. _____
10 Summer starts at June. _____
11 My favourite programme starts on ten o'clock. _____
12 I go to school with bus. _____

6B GRAMMAR Past simple: *be* and *can*

I can talk about my past.

1 Look at the calendar. Write sentences about Natalie and Chris. Use the past simple of *be* (affirmative or negative).

```
● ● ●                    Calendar
```

Day	Chris	Natalie
Mon	Budapest	Madrid
Tues	Rome	Lisbon
Wed	Athens	Athens
Thurs	Paris	Prague
Fri	Istanbul	Budapest
Sat	Dublin	Dublin

1 Natalie / Madrid / Monday
  Natalie was in Madrid on Monday.

2 Chris and Natalie / Athens / Wednesday

3 Chris / Lisbon / Tuesday

4 Natalie / Dublin / Saturday

5 Chris and Natalie / Dublin / Friday

6 Natalie / Budapest / Monday

2 Where were Chris and Natalie last week? Complete the questions, then write answers.

1 __Was__ Chris in Budapest on Monday?
  Yes, he was.

2 Where __was__ Natalie on Tuesday?
  She was in Lisbon.

3 _____ Natalie in Budapest on Wednesday?

4 _____ Chris in Istanbul on Friday?

5 Where _____ Natalie and Chris on Wednesday?

6 _____ Chris and Natalie in Athens on Thursday?

7 _____ Chris and Natalie in Dublin on Saturday?

3 Look at the chart. Write questions and answers about Martha and Liam. Use the past simple of *be* and *can*.

	Martha	Liam
write his / her name	age 3	age 4
ride a bike	age 6	age 5
swim	age 7	age 7

1 Liam / write his name / four?
  Could Liam write his name when he was four?
  Yes, he could.

2 Liam / swim / six?

3 Martha / ride a bike / seven?

4 Martha and Liam / swim / seven?

5 Martha and Liam / ride a bike / four?

4 Complete the dialogue. Use the past simple form of *be* and *can* (affirmative, negative or interrogative).

Mike Where ¹_____ you last weekend?
I ²_____ phone you on your mobile.

Rachel Sorry, my mobile ³_____ on.
I ⁴_____ in the USA. The calls are very expensive!

Mike ⁵_____ you in New York?

Rachel No, we ⁶_____ . We ⁷_____ in Chicago.

Mike What ⁸_____ it like?

Rachel It ⁹_____ amazing. On Saturday morning we ¹⁰_____ at the top of the Willis Tower. But we ¹¹_____ see much because the weather ¹²_____ very good.

Challenge!

Where were you at these times? Write three sentences.

1 at seven o'clock yesterday evening

2 at ten o'clock on Saturday morning

3 at three o'clock yesterday afternoon

6C
CULTURE Teen adventure

I can talk about tourist attractions in a city.

Revision: Student's Book page 60

1 Complete the pairs of adjectives with opposite meanings.

1 safe – d_____
2 easy – d_____
3 clean – d_____
4 cheap – e_____
5 modern – o_____
6 fast – s_____
7 fantastic – t_____

2 Complete the sentences with adjectives from exercise 1.

1 It's _____ to travel around in London. There are lots of buses and underground trains.
2 You need a lot of money in London. Everything is very _____ .
3 There are _____ views from the top of the London Eye.
4 Big cities are often _____ , but London is quite clean.
5 There are many old buildings in London, but there are also a lot of _____ ones.

3 Complete the text on the tourist information website with the words below.

a   and   are   do   don't   ~~from~~   of   or   to   to

Come to San Francisco!

- Take a boat trip to Alcatraz Island in San Francisco Bay. It was once a prison for very dangerous criminals. Tourists ¹_from_ all over the world visit it and listen ²_____ the stories of the famous prisoners.

- Visit the amazing Golden Gate Bridge. It's 227 metres high and nearly three kilometres long. You can walk ³_____ cycle across the bridge. See fantastic views ⁴_____ the city.

- Don't miss the Aquarium of the Bay! Walk in a tunnel under the water and see the sharks ⁵_____ stingrays that live in San Francisco Bay.

- Walk along the beautiful Ocean Beach. Enjoy the sunshine and take ⁶_____ picnic. You can surf there, but ⁷_____ swim as it isn't safe. Bring a skateboard or rollerblades and skate along the path next ⁸_____ the beach!

- ⁹_____ you like shopping? Then come to Chestnut Street. There ¹⁰_____ small shops and big shops, expensive shops and cheap shops. There's something for everyone!

4 Match places 1–5 with sentences a–f. There is one sentence that you do not need.

1 Alcatraz Island ☐
2 Golden Gate Bridge ☐
3 Aquarium of the Bay ☐
4 Ocean Beach ☐
5 Chestnut Street ☐

a You can go skateboarding and rollerblading.
b You can see animals that live in the bay.
c You can go shopping.
d You can swim safely.
e You can see great views.
f You can visit a prison.

5 🎧 **LISTENING 32** Listen to Alice and Jake planning a visit to Dublin. Complete the diary with words from the box.

art gallery   climb a mountain   market   picnic
go swimming   shopping centre   zoo

	Morning	Afternoon
Saturday		
Sunday		

Challenge!

INTERNET RESEARCH Find out about a city that you would like to visit. Write three things that you can do and see there.

1 _____
2 _____
3 _____

6D GRAMMAR Past simple affirmative: regular verbs

I can talk about past events.

1 Write the past simple forms in the correct group.

| chat | phone | plan | play | reply | smile | tidy | walk |

add -ed	1 _____	2 _____
add -d	3 _____	4 _____
-y → -ied	5 _____	6 _____
double consonant and add -ed	7 _____	8 _____

2 Complete the sentences. Use the past simple form of the verbs in the box.

| chat | cry | dance | invite | start | study | wash |

1 I _____ twenty friends to my party.

2 I _____ to my friends at the café.

3 My dad _____ German at school.

4 Harriet _____ at the end of the sad film.

5 Sam _____ with Emma at the night club.

6 George _____ his hair this morning.

7 Our English lesson _____ at 9.30.

3 Complete the story. Use the past simple form of the verbs in brackets.

A police officer was in a park in the centre of the town. She ¹_____ (notice) a boy and girl with a baby elephant. The police officer was very surprised. 'What are you doing with that elephant?' she ²_____ (ask). 'You should take it to the zoo.'

'OK,' the boy and girl ³_____ (agree), and they ⁴_____ (hurry) off.

The next day, the police officer was in town again when the same boy and girl ⁵_____ (appear). The elephant was still with them. The police officer was annoyed.

'Hey!' she called, 'You ⁶_____ (promise) to take that elephant to the zoo!'

'Yes,' ⁷_____ (reply) the children, 'we ⁸_____ (visit) the zoo yesterday and the elephant ⁹_____ (enjoy) it. So today we're taking him to the museum.'

4 Complete the time expressions with the words in the box.

| afternoon | ago | before | last | month | years | yesterday |

1 four years _____

2 _____ night

3 yesterday _____

4 two _____ ago

5 _____ morning

6 last _____

7 the day _____ yesterday

5 Rewrite the sentences. Use the past simple and the time expressions in brackets.

1 I play volleyball at weekends. (last weekend)
   I played volleyball last weekend.

2 I cycle to school every day. (yesterday morning)
   _____

3 I usually stay in on Sunday evenings. (last night)
   _____

4 Andy sometimes tidies his bedroom on Sunday evenings. (on Saturday evening)
   _____

5 The bus stops outside our house. (five minutes ago)
   _____

6 I listen to the radio every morning. (yesterday afternoon)
   _____

7 It always rains a lot in Scotland. (last month)
   _____

8 School finishes at four o'clock. (half an hour ago)
   _____

Challenge!

Write five sentences. Use the past simple and five time expressions from exercises 4 and 5.

1 _____

2 _____

3 _____

4 _____

5 _____

I can understand a story about a bad experience.

Revision: Student's Book page 63

1 **Complete the adjectives to describe feelings.**

1 Joe has got a girlfriend. He's really h_____ !

2 Cathy was t_____ so she decided to go to bed.

3 I stayed out late last Saturday. My parents were w_____ .

4 Sam was really s_____ when he saw the dangerous dog.

5 I'm b_____ . There's nothing to do!

6 Dad is very busy. Don't be s_____ if he gets home very late this evening.

7 Kate's n_____ because she's got an important exam tomorrow.

8 I'm h_____ . Can I have something to eat?

9 My mum was a_____ because my bedroom was very untidy.

3 **Read the story again. Choose the correct answers.**

1 Charlie works in **Chicago** / **Los Angeles**.

2 Charlie's parents live in **Chicago** / **Los Angeles**.

3 Charlie decided to **fly** / **post himself** to Chicago.

4 He **could** / **couldn't** eat or drink on the plane.

5 Charlie arrived in Chicago **the next day** / **two days later**.

6 **Charlie's parents** / **Mike Lincoln** phoned the police.

4 **TRANSLATION** Write a summary of the story in your language.

_____

_____

_____

_____

_____

_____

2 **Read the story. Match paragraphs 1–7 with pictures A–G.**

1 Charlie Webber, 20, is a postman. He's from Chicago, but he works in Los Angeles. One Friday afternoon, he was at work. He wasn't very happy, and he wanted to go home to Chicago for the weekend and see his parents. ☐

2 Plane tickets from Los Angeles to Chicago are very expensive, so he decided to get into a big box and post himself to Chicago by airmail. It was the cheapest way to fly! ☐

3 Later that day, he was on the plane to Chicago. He was in a box for fifteen hours with no food or water. Nobody noticed him in the box. ☐

4 The next day, the box arrived in Chicago. Mike Lincoln, a postman in Chicago, carried the large box from his van to Mr and Mrs Webber's house. ☐

5 When he arrived at their house, he suddenly noticed two eyes in the box. He decided there was a dead person inside, so he called the police. ☐

6 A few minutes later, Charlie opened the box and shouted, 'Surprise!' ☐

7 After that, the police arrived. They asked Charlie lots of questions. In the end, Charlie stayed in prison for the rest of the weekend! ☐

I can ask for detailed information about tourist places.

1 LISTENING 33 **Complete the dialogue with the lines in the box. Then listen and check.**

> You're welcome. Goodbye.
>
> Good afternoon. Natural History Museum.
>
> It's $10 for adults and $6 for children under fourteen.
>
> It's in Jacob Street, next to the concert hall.
>
> Sure. What would you like to know?
>
> We open at ten o'clock and close at half past five.

Clerk   1_____

Carl   Good afternoon. I'd like some information about the museum, please.

Clerk   2_____

Carl   What time do you open and close?

Clerk   3_____
        But we don't sell tickets after four o'clock.

Carl   How much are the tickets?

Clerk   5_____

Carl   Where is the museum exactly?

Clerk   6_____

Carl   OK. Thanks very much.

Clerk   7_____

Carl   Goodbye.

2 LISTENING 34 **Listen to the dialogue. Complete the information.**

Science Museum

Opening times: _____ until _____
Last entry: _____
Tickets: Adults: $_____
            Children under _____ : $6
            Students: $_____
Finding us: Lincoln Street, next to _____

3 **Write these questions and sentences in a different way.**

1 How can I help you?
   What would you like to know?

2 I'd like some information about the museum, please.
   Can you _____ ?

3 How much are the tickets?
   _____ does it _____ ?

4 What time do you open and close?
   What are _____ ?

5 We don't sell tickets after five o'clock.
   The last _____ .

6 Where is the gallery exactly?
   Can you _____ ?

4 **Write a dialogue like the one in exercise 1. Use the information on the poster and sentences from exercises 1 and 3.**

MUSEUM OF MODERN ART

Opening hours:	9.30 a.m. to 6 p.m.
Last entry:	5 p.m.
Tickets:	**Adults:** $15
	Children (under 12): $10
Finding us:	Washington Street, opposite the train station

Clerk   *Good afternoon, Museum of Modern Art. How can I help you?*

Jo   _____

Clerk   _____

Jo   _____

Clerk   _____

Jo   _____

Clerk   _____

Jo   _____

Clerk   _____

Jo   _____

Clerk   _____

Jo   _____

Challenge!

INTERNET RESEARCH **Find a website for an interesting museum in Britain or the USA. Find out the information below.**

1 Name of the museum: _____

2 Opening times: _____

3 Cost of tickets: _____

4 Where is the museum exactly? (name of street):
   _____

Preparation

1 Complete the phrases with the words in the box. Each pair of phrases has a similar meaning.

message   news   phoned   pleased   shame
so much   sorry   thank

1 Just a quick note to _____ you for …
Thank you _____ for …

2 I was really _____ to hear that …
It's fantastic / great _____ !

3 Harry _____ from the …
There's a _____ from Jason.

4 It's such a _____ that …
I was so _____ to hear that …

2 Match the pairs of phrases (1–4) in exercise 1 with the types of message (a–d).

a   a phone message   ☐

b   a message of congratulation   ☐

c   a message of sympathy   ☐

d   a thank-you note   ☐

3 Match the words to make phrases you can use in messages.

1	What	f	a	fantastic achievement.
2	Get	☐	b	was really kind of you.
3	It's a	☐	c	urgent.
4	We're very proud	☐	d	done!
5	It's	☐	e	well soon.
6	We're all	☐	f	a lovely surprise!
7	Well	☐	g	on his mobile.
8	Please phone him	☐	h	thinking of you.
9	It	☐	i	of you.

4 Write a phrase from exercise 3 for the situations below. (Sometimes more than one answer is possible.)

1 Your friend passed an exam.

_____

2 Your granddad is in hospital.

_____

3 You received a gift voucher from your aunt.

_____

4 Your sister phoned. She wants dad to phone her.

_____

5 Complete the messages with sentences a–d.

a   I use it every day.

b   He's got the book you wanted.

c   I hear that you all played really well.

d   I hope that you feel better soon.

> Mum,
> Mr Black from the library called. 1_____
> You can get it tomorrow.
> His phone number is 578990.
> Marion

> Luke,
> It's great that your team were first in the football tournament.
> 2_____ We're very proud of you!
> With love from Grandma

> Dear Granddad,
> I was so sorry to hear that you aren't well.
> 3_____ I'll come and see you tomorrow.
> Get well soon!
> Love, Tom

> Zoe,
> Thank you so much for the MP3 player! It was really kind of you.
> 4_____ Hope to see you soon.
> Love, Frances

Writing guide

6 Choose a situation and write a message. Use phrases from exercises 1 and 3 to help you.

1 **Congratulation:** A friend passed an important exam.

2 **Sympathy:** Your cousin is in hospital.

3 **Thanks:** Your received a CD for your birthday from your uncle.

4 **Phone message:** Your sister's friend phoned. She wants to go to the cinema this evening with your sister. Leave a message for your sister.

_____

_____

_____

_____

_____

CHECK YOUR WORK

Have you:

☐ included phrases from exercises 1 and 3?

☐ checked your spelling and grammar?

1 Where do the people go? Write the place.

1 I want to buy some stamps. _____

2 I want to listen to classical music. _____

3 I want to catch a bus. _____

4 I want to see some paintings. _____

5 I want to borrow a book. _____

Mark: ___ /5

2 Complete the words in the sentences.

1 I'm hungry. Let's o_____ a pizza.

2 If I'm not at home, please l_____ a message.

3 On Friday evening my friends and I usually go dancing at a n_____ c_____ .

4 You can p_____ the car in the car park near the school.

Mark: ___ /4

3 Match the sentence halves.

1 School starts ☐   a in June.

2 Marco lives in Dublin, but he's ☐   b by car.

3 Summer starts ☐   c from Italy.

4 My dad goes to work ☐   d at eight o'clock.

Mark: ___ /4

4 Complete the sentences. Use the past simple form of *be*.

1 The weather _____ bad yesterday, so we stayed at home.

2 '_____ Jason and Kelly at school this morning?' 'No, they _____ .'

3 Peter _____ at the cinema. He was at the theatre.

4 Joe and Kate _____ in London last week. They visited Buckingham Palace.

Mark: ___ /4

5 Complete the sentences. Use the past simple form of *can*, affirmative or negative, and the verbs in the box.

| go   play   sleep   walk |

1 We _____ tennis because the weather was bad.

2 David _____ before he was one year old.

3 Tom _____ to the cinema because he was ill.

4 I was very tired, but I _____ .

Mark: ___ /4

6 Complete the text. Use the past simple form of the verbs in the box.

| chat   listen   phone   stay   tidy   watch |

Yesterday evening I [1]_____ at home. I [2]_____ television and then I [3]_____ to music on my MP3 player. After dinner, I [4]_____ my friend Becky and we [5]_____ for an hour. Then I [6]_____ my bedroom.

Mark: ___ /6

7 Complete the time expressions. Use *a*, *e*, and *o*.

1 th__ d__y b__f__r__ y__st__rd__y

2 thr____ m__nths __g__

3 l__st w____k

Mark: ___ /3

Total: ___ /30

I can …

Read the statements. Think about your progress and tick one of the boxes.

★ = I need more practice.   ★★ = I sometimes find this difficult.

★★★ = No problem!

	★	★★	★★★
I can describe places in a town. (SB p.58)			
I can talk about my past. (SB p.59)			
I can talk about tourist attractions in a city. (SB p.60)			
I can talk about past events. (SB p.61)			
I can understand a story about a bad experience. (SB p.62)			
I can ask for detailed information about tourist places. (SB p.64)			
I can write different kinds of note. (SB p.65)			

PREPARATION: Reading

1 Match the words (1–6) with the definitions (a–f).

1	boring	a	a part of a train where people sit
2	pick	b	not difficult
3	easy	c	not expensive
4	begin	d	not interesting
5	carriage	e	start to do something or start to happen
6	cheap	f	take a flower, fruit or vegetable from the place where it grows

EXAM STRATEGY

- Read the task carefully and read the text for general meaning.
- Identify the paragraph in the text that will help you decide about each true/false statement.
- Decide if the statements 1–6 are true or false.

EXAM TASK – Reading

Read the story. Decide if statements 1–6 are true (T) or false (F).

South for the winter

I never stay in one country for a long time. It gets boring. I like to move on, see new places, meet different people. It's a good life most of the time. When I need money, I get a job. I can do most things – hotel and restaurant work, building work, picking fruit. In Europe you can pick fruit most of the year. It's not easy work, but the money's not bad.

I like to go south for the winter. Life is easier in the sun, and northern Europe can get very cold in the winter. Last year I was in Venice for October. I did some work in a hotel for three weeks, then I began slowly to move south. I always go by train when I can. I like trains. You can walk about on a train, and you meet a lot of people.

I left Venice and went on to Trieste. There I got a cheap ticket for the slow train to Sofia, in Bulgaria. This train goes all the way down Eastern Europe and takes a long time – a day and a half. But that didn't matter to me.

The train left Trieste at nine o'clock on a Thursday morning. There weren't many people on it at first, but at Zagreb more people got on. Two girls went along the corridor, past my carriage. They looked through the door, but they didn't come in. Then an old woman came in, sat down and went to sleep. The two girls came back along the corridor and looked into the carriage again. The train left Zagreb and I looked out of the window for ten minutes, then I went to sleep too.

When I opened my eyes again, the two girls were in my carriage. They looked friendly, so I said, 'Hello.'

1 The writer is a traveller. _____
2 The writer prefers cold to hot weather. _____
3 The writer's favourite means of transport is the train because it's fast. _____
4 The writer was in a hurry when he left Trieste. _____
5 Two girls joined the writer after the train left Zagreb. _____
6 The writer started the conversation with the girls because they were pretty. _____

PREPARATION: Listening

1 Read the task, the sentences and the multiple-choice options carefully.
2 Based on the information in the task, decide if these sentences are true or false.
  1 The listening is a monologue (a single person speaking). _____
  2 Kitty Williams has probably experienced life in two places: London and Hollywood. _____
  3 Kitty talks about food and lifestyle. _____

EXAM TASK – Listening

🎧 LISTENING 35 Listen to an interview with actress Kitty Williams. Choose the correct answer (A–C) for questions 1–5.

1 Kitty Williams's life in Hollywood is
  A healthier than in London.
  B very busy.
  C very stressful.

2 In Hollywood Kitty Williams eats
  A the same food as in London.
  B only vegetables.
  C no meat.

3 Kitty finds it easy to have a healthy diet in Hollywood because
  A the temperature is always high.
  B restaurants offer a lot of choice.
  C she doesn't like butter or mayonnaise.

4 Kitty Williams thinks running is
  A very tiring.
  B a good way to start a day.
  C relaxing after a long day of work.

5 Kitty misses London because
  A she likes going to the gym with her friends.
  B she can eat chips or pasta there.
  C it is more entertaining than Hollywood.

EXAM STRATEGY: Use of English

Read the text through once to get a general understanding before trying to choose the right answers.

EXAM TASK – Use of English

Choose the correct alternatives.

Are pescetarians vegetarians? Most vegetarians don't think so. People ¹*start / started* using the word pescetarian in the 1990s to describe a person who doesn't eat ²*some / any* meat but does eat fish and other seafood. Most pescetarians believe they are vegetarians, but the Vegetarian Society believe that to be a true veggie you ³*shouldn't / should* eat any living animal. Some pescetarians ⁴*don't / didn't* eat meat because they don't like it, some believe that we ⁵*should / shouldn't* keep animals for food but think that they should eat some fish for a ⁶*balanced / balancing* diet. Some start by being pescetarians and then become full vegetarians.

My friend Pete ⁷*were / was* a vegetarian for years. He didn't eat any meat or fish. But two years ago he began eating fish again. When I asked him why, he said he was a vegetarian because he ⁸*not liked / didn't like* the taste of meat, not because he thought it was wrong to kill animals. But he ⁹*travelled / travels* to Spain and tried some salmon and prawns by accident – and loved them. So is he a vegetarian? He says he isn't, he ¹⁰*called / calls* himself a 'non-meat eater'.

EXAM STRATEGY: Writing

- Plan your text carefully. You only have 100–120 words and you must cover four points.
- First, write a few notes for each point.
- Then, write a short paragraph about each point.
- Remember: you must also write a short introduction and a summary/conclusion at the end.

EXAM TASK – Writing

Imagine that in September your school opened a new school canteen. Write a short article (100–120 words) for the school magazine about it. In the article say:

- what is the place like
- what sort of dishes you can usually choose from
- if you think they cook healthy meals
- how students like it

PREPARATION: Speaking

1 Match each expression below to the correct picture.

> in a restaurant   a waitress   serve the customer
> seem to be happy   turkey   a family dinner
> celebrate Thanksgiving Day   have breakfast
> in the dining room   pleasant and friendly atmosphere

2 Complete the sentences with the following expressions.

> they both show people enjoying their meals
> the man is having breakfast on his own
> people having a meal   a man having breakfast
> shows a family dinner

a Both pictures show _____ .
b The first picture shows _____ ,
whereas the second picture _____ .
c The two pictures are similar because _____ .
d There are also some differences. For example,
_____ , while there are
many people enjoying the family dinner together.

EXAM STRATEGY

- When you describe a picture you must say: *who* is in the picture, *where* they are and *what* they are doing.
- Read the task carefully. Look at the picture and think what vocabulary you may need to describe and compare the pictures.
- During your preparation time make notes about the people, where they are, and what they are doing.
- Think about arguments you are going to use to answer the second part of the question.
- To express your opinion use phrases in the Functions Bank page 108.

EXAM TASK – Speaking

Compare and contrast the pictures below. Then say which of the two situations you like better and why. Do you think that the food the people in the pictures are eating is good for them? Why / Why not?

7A VOCABULARY AND LISTENING

On the map
I can talk about people's countries and nationalities.

1 What are these countries? Label the maps.

I _ _ _ _ _

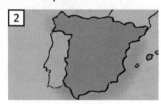

S _ _ _ _ _

B _ _ _ _ _ _

J _ _ _ _ _

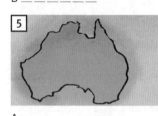

A _ _ _ _ _ _ _ _ _

S _ _ _ _ _ _

2 Where are these cities? Complete the names of the countries. Then write the nationalities. Use the Internet to help you.

1	Moscow	*Russia*	*Russian*
2	Vilnius	L_____	_____
3	Minsk	B_____	_____
4	Kiev	U_____	_____
5	Bratislava	S_____	_____
6	Bucharest	R_____	_____
7	Warsaw	P_____	_____
8	Istanbul	T_____	_____
9	São Paulo	B_____	_____
10	Beijing	C_____	_____
11	Cairo	E_____	_____
12	Berlin	G_____	_____

3 🎧 **LISTENING 36** Listen to the conversations. Write the nationalities.

1 Marko is _Croatian_ .
  Lucy is _____ .

2 Thomas is _____ .
  Maria is _____ .

3 Jan is _____ .
  Ana is _____ .

4 Hugo is _____ .
  Frith is _____ .

Challenge!

INTERNET RESEARCH How many more countries and nationalities can you add?

Country	Nationality
_____	_____
_____	_____
_____	_____
_____	_____

VOCABULARY BUILDER (PART 2): *MAKE, DO, HAVE AND TAKE.* >>SB PAGE 137<<

4 Complete the chart with the words in the box.

a dream   friends   homework   housework
a photo   a science lesson   a speech   a train

do	have
geography	lunch
1 _____	5 _____
2 _____	6 _____

make	take
a phone call	an exam
3 _____	7 _____
4 _____	8 _____

5 Complete the sentences with the correct form of *make, do, have,* or *take.*

1 We don't _do_ French at school.

2 Let's _____ a train to London, not a bus.

3 My dad's going to _____ a speech at my sister's wedding.

4 Do you have to _____ an exam at the end of the year?

5 I need to _____ a phone call. Can I use your mobile?

6 We _____ an English lesson after lunch.

7 My dad never _____ the housework.

8 I usually _____ lunch in the school canteen.

1 Write the past simple form of the verbs.

1 begin _____   5 grow _____
2 break _____   6 have _____
3 buy _____   7 say _____
4 take _____   8 sing _____

2 Complete the sentences with verbs from exercise 1.

1 My mum _____ some pizzas at the supermarket.
2 'Good morning, everyone,' _____ the teacher.
3 Liam _____ lunch in a café in town.
4 I _____ to study English when I was eight.
5 Martin _____ a song at the school concert.
6 Last year, we _____ potatoes in our garden.
7 David _____ a train from London to Edinburgh.
8 Oh, no! Who _____ this glass?

3 Put the time expressions in order, with the most recent first.

last month	~~last night~~	last week	last year
the day before yesterday		three months ago	
two years ago	yesterday afternoon		yesterday morning

1 <u>last night</u>   6 _____
2 _____   7 _____
3 _____   8 _____
4 _____   9 _____
5 _____

4 Rewrite the sentences in the past tense. Add the time expression in brackets.

1 I wear trainers to school. (yesterday)
  <u>I wore trainers to school yesterday.</u>

2 Sally and I take the bus to school. (the day before yesterday)
  _____
  _____

3 Susan sleeps until ten o'clock. (yesterday morning)
  _____
  _____

4 My dad does a lot of housework. (last week)
  _____
  _____

5 I spend a lot of money on clothes. (last weekend)
  _____
  _____

6 My mum makes cakes. (yesterday afternoon)
  _____
  _____

5 🎧 LISTENING 37 Complete the text. Use the past simple form of the verbs in brackets. Then listen and check.

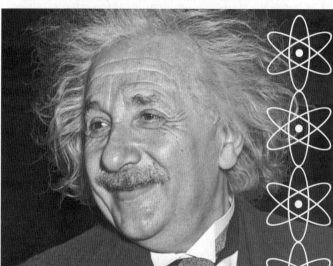

ALBERT EINSTEIN [1]_____ (be) born in 1879 in Germany. He [2]_____ (hate) school. His teachers [3]_____ (think) he wasn't very clever, and he [4]_____ (leave) school at the age of fifteen. But he [5]_____ (love) science, and he [6]_____ (read) lots of books on his own. When he was 23, he [7]_____ (move) to Switzerland and [8]_____ (get) a job in an office. In his free time, he [9]_____ (write) about physics and the universe, and he [10]_____ (send) his work to universities. In 1914, he [11]_____ (return) to Germany and [12]_____ (become) a professor at a university in Berlin. There, he developed new ideas about time, space and atoms. In 1921, he [13]_____ (win) the Nobel Prize for Physics. In 1933, he [14]_____ (decide) to leave Germany and [15]_____ (go) to the USA, where he [16]_____ (live) for the rest of his life. He [17]_____ (die) in 1955 at the age of 76. Few people [18]_____ (can) understand his ideas at that time, but now they are an important part of physics.

Challenge!

Write five sentences about yourself. Use the past simple and time expressions from exercise 3.

1 _____
2 _____
3 _____
4 _____
5 _____

CULTURE Changing the world

I can understand a text about a historical event.

Revision: Student's Book page 70

1 Choose the correct prepositions in these sentences about Rosa Parks.

1 Rosa Parks lived **in / on** the south **of / to** the USA.

2 She went **at / to** work **by / on** bus.

3 On buses, black people had to sit **after / at** the back.

4 Parks refused to give her seat on the bus **at / to** a white man.

5 Black people stopped using the buses in Alabama **by / for** 381 days. **After / To** a year, the state changed the law.

2 Read the text opposite and answer the questions.

1 When and where was Nelson Mandela born?

_____

2 How many children did his father have?

_____

3 What did he study?

_____

4 What did the ANC want?

_____

5 What happened in 1960?

_____

6 How long did Mandela spend in prison?

_____

7 What did he win in 1993?

_____

8 When did he become President of South Africa?

_____

3 🎧 **LISTENING 38** Listen to three people talking about their heroes. Choose the correct answers.

1 At what age did Adele first start singing?

a three **b** four **c** five

2 Who put Adele's first songs on the Internet?

a Adele **b** Adele's mum **c** Adele's friend

3 When was Lionel Messi born?

a 1986 **b** 1987 **c** 1988

4 How old was Messi when he played his first match for Barcelona?

a 13 **b** 15 **c** 16

5 How old was Emma's grandmother when she died?

a 91 **b** 81 **c** 71

6 Where was Emma's grandmother's during the war?

a Liverpool **b** Leeds **c** London

Nelson Mandela

Nelson Mandela was born in 1918 in a small South African village. His father had four wives and nine children. Mandela was a clever boy and took his school exams early. Then he studied law and became a lawyer in 1952.

At that time in South Africa, black people and white people were not equal. Mandela became a leader of the African National Congress. The ANC wanted equal rights for black people. It was a peaceful organisation. But in 1960, the police killed 69 black people in the town of Sharpeville. After that, the ANC began to use violence against the government. In 1962, the police arrested Mandela and he went to prison for life. He became a hero, and black South Africans continued to fight for equality.

The world was also against the South African government. Eventually, in 1990, President FW de Klerk decided to change things. He released Mandela from prison after 27 years. Three years later, he and Mandela won the Nobel Peace Prize. And in 1994, South Africans chose Mandela to be the country's first black president.

Challenge!

INTERNET RESEARCH Find out about a famous person that you admire. Write five sentences. Use the past simple form of the verbs in the box, or your own ideas.

| be born become die get a job get married |
| live play win write |

1 _____

2 _____

3 _____

4 _____

5 _____

I can say what did and didn't happen in the past.

1 Make the sentences negative.

1 Jake phoned Sarah yesterday evening.
  Jake didn't phone Sarah yesterday evening.

2 George went to London last weekend.
  _____

3 Joe wore his new jacket yesterday.
  _____

4 Pete invited Fred to his birthday party.
  _____

5 You sent me an email.
  _____

6 Wendy left home before nine o'clock.
  _____

7 My dad studied German at school.
  _____

2 Write true sentences about what you did last weekend. Use the past simple, affirmative or negative, and the prompts.

1 make a phone call
  I made a phone call. / I didn't make a phone call.

2 go to the theatre
  _____

3 help with the housework
  _____

4 play basketball
  _____

5 read a book
  _____

3 Put the words in the correct order to make questions. Then write true answers.

1 you / last night? / go / did / when / to bed
  When did you go to bed last night?
  I went to bed at ten o'clock.

2 come / how / this morning? / did / you / to school
  _____
  _____

3 do / what / you / last Saturday morning? / did
  _____
  _____

4 last Sunday? / you / what time / did / get up
  _____
  _____

5 this morning? / you / what / did / for breakfast / have
  _____
  _____

4 🎧 LISTENING 39 Listen to Rosie asking Rob about his weekend and complete the sentences. Use the past simple form, affirmative or negative, of the verbs in brackets.

1 Rob _didn't have_ a good time at the weekend. (have)
2 Rob and Sam _____ football. (play)
3 Rob and Sam _____ to the cinema. (go)
4 Rob and Sam _____ a film. (see)
5 Rob and Sam _____ the right bus. (take)

5 Now write questions and short answers. Use your answers to exercise 4.

1 Did Rob have a good time at the weekend?
  No, he didn't.

2 _____
  _____

3 _____
  _____

4 _____
  _____

5 _____
  _____

6 Find the mistakes in these sentences. Rewrite them correctly.

1 Sally catched the bus to town. ✗
  Sally caught the bus to town.

2 When you come home last night? ✗
  _____

3 Did Mum made a cake yesterday? ✗
  _____

4 Kevin not wore jeans to school. ✗
  _____

5 We didn't stayed in last night. We went out. ✗
  _____

6 'Did Jamie watch TV last night?' 'Yes, he watched.' ✗
  _____

Challenge!

Write three more quiz questions for your classmates. Use *when*, *where*, and *what*.

1 When did Poland join the European Union?
2 _____
3 _____
4 _____

I can understand biographies of famous artists.

Revision: Student's Book page 72

1 Complete the sentences about Pablo Picasso with the words in the box.

born	died	had	got	got	left	retire	went

1 Picasso was _____ in Spain in 1881.
2 He moved to Barcelona when his dad _____ a job at an art college there.
3 When he was 16, Picasso _____ school and _____ to art college in Madrid.
4 Picasso _____ married twice. He _____ four children.
5 Picasso didn't _____ . He worked nearly every day until he _____ in 1973.

2 Read the text opposite. Choose the correct answers.

1 Dalí painted pictures of
  a real life.
  b his ideas and dreams.
  c all the people that he knew.

2 He started drawing lessons when he was
  a ten.
  b fifteen.
  c eighteen.

3 He left art college because
  a he wanted to go to Paris.
  b he was tired of his teachers.
  c he didn't want to continue painting.

4 Dalí
  a spent most of the 1940s in Spain.
  b returned to Spain at the end of the 1940s.
  c lived in the USA from 1948.

5 Dalí
  a stopped painting and made films and furniture.
  b bought a museum for his paintings.
  c wore strange clothes.

3 Put the events of Dalí's life in the correct order.

  a ☐ He went to the USA.
  b ☐ He had his first art exhibition.
  c ☐ He built a museum.
  d ☐ He returned to Spain.
  e ☐ He went to Paris and met Picasso.
  f ☐ He was born in 1904.
  g ☐ He went to art college.
  h ☐ He had drawing lessons.

Salvador Dalí

Salvador Dalí was a very famous Surrealist painter. He didn't paint pictures of real life. He painted pictures of his ideas and dreams. Everybody knows his paintings and he is an important person for many of today's artists and designers.

Dalí was born in Figueres, Spain, in 1904. He was good at art from a very early age and he had drawing lessons from the age of ten. When he was fifteen, he had his first art exhibition. At the age of eighteen, he went to art college in Madrid. Three years later, Dalí was tired of his teachers and they asked him to leave the college. He wanted to learn new things, so he went to Paris and met Picasso.

Dalí became well known in Europe and America for his interesting paintings. He spent most of the 1940s in the USA, and he returned to Figueres in 1948. He continued to paint, and he also made films and designed furniture. In 1960, he built a museum for his own paintings. He was famous for his big personality, funny clothes and crazy ideas. People thought he was either mad or wonderful. He died at 84, and his ideas changed art, design and advertising for ever.

Challenge!

INTERNET RESEARCH Find out about one of the artists below, or another artist. Write a short biography. Use the phrases in exercise 1 and the verbs in the box.

1 Leonardo da Vinci (1452–1519)
2 Claude Monet (1840–1926)
3 Andy Warhol (1928–1987)

drew	lived	painted	studied

_____
_____
_____
_____
_____
_____
_____
_____
_____
_____

EVERYDAY ENGLISH Talking about your weekend

I can talk about what happened at the weekend.

1 Complete the free-time activities with the verbs in the box.

| go on a   go out for   go out with   go to a |
| go to the   listen   make   surf   watch   watch |

1 _____ cinema / theatre
2 _____ gig / nightclub / friend's house / party
3 _____ to music
4 _____ TV
5 _____ social-networking site
6 _____ a DVD
7 _____ friends
8 _____ the Internet
9 _____ a meal
10 _____ phone calls

2 Complete the expressions with the letters *a, e, o, u* and *y*. Do they express sympathy or interest? Tick ✓ the correct boxes.

	Sympathy	Interest
1 C__ __l!	☐	☐
2 Wh__t a sh__m__!	☐	☐
3 P__ __r y__ __!	☐	☐
4 __h d__ __r!	☐	☐
5 S__ __nds f__n!	☐	☐
6 R__ __ll__?	☐	☐
7 W__w!	☐	☐
8 __h n__!	☐	☐

3 🎧 **LISTENING 40** **SPEAKING** Listen and react using expressions from exercise 2. Use a different expression each time.

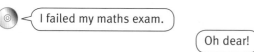 I failed my maths exam.

 Oh dear!

 I won £100 last weekend!

 Wow!

4 Put the words in the correct order to make questions.

1 you / what / at / do / the / weekend / did / ?

_____

2 your / how / weekend / was / ?

_____

3 was / why / that / oh, / ?

_____

4 did / Saturday / you / do / what / night / on / ?

_____

5 🎧 **LISTENING 41** Complete the dialogue with the questions from exercise 4. Then listen and check.

Marcus ¹____

Nancy It wasn't great.

Marcus ²____

Nancy Well, on Saturday afternoon I went shopping and I left my purse on the bus.

Marcus What a disaster! ³____

Nancy I went out for a meal with my family, but I hated the food.

Marcus Oh dear!

Nancy ⁴____

Marcus I went to London to see my cousin. We visited a museum and had a picnic in Hyde Park.

Nancy Sounds fun!

6 Put a tick ✓ if the event was good. Put a cross ✗ if the event was bad.

1 We went to a nightclub. We had a great time.   ✓
2 We saw a football match. My favourite team lost.   ☐
3 My dad had an accident. He's in hospital.   ☐
4 I took my driving test. I passed!   ☐
5 We went to the cinema. The film was really good.   ☐
6 I went to town. I lost my mobile phone.   ☐

7 Write a dialogue like the one in exercise 5. Use ideas from exercises 1 and 6 or your own ideas.

Jess   *How was your weekend?* _____

Ryan   _____

Jess   _____

Ryan   _____

Jess   _____

Ryan   _____

Jess   _____

Ryan   _____

Jess   _____

Ryan   _____

I can write an email describing my weekend.

Preparation

1 Complete the verb and noun collocations with the words in the box.

bed   an email   friends   friend's house   go
go for   have   play   read

1 _____ shopping
2 meet some _____
3 _____ lunch at a café
4 write _____
5 _____ a book
6 go to _____ early
7 _____ a walk
8 stay at a _____
9 _____ basketball

2 Match 1–13 with a–m to make useful phrases for emails.

1 Look after   [j]   a hello.
2 Email   [ ]   b to you soon.
3 I hope   [ ]   c hear from you!
4 Chris says   [ ]   d you're well.
5 Say hi   [ ]   e your weekend?
6 Speak   [ ]   f Emma
7 How are   [ ]   g I have to go.
8 Thanks for   [ ]   h care.
9 How was   [ ]   i me soon.
10 Great to   [ ]   j ~~yourself.~~
11 Anyway,   [ ]   k your email.
12 Take   [ ]   l things with you?
13 Love,   [ ]   m to David.

3 TRANSLATION Translate the phrases in exercise 2.

1 _____
2 _____
3 _____
4 _____
5 _____
6 _____
7 _____
8 _____
9 _____
10 _____
11 _____
12 _____
13 _____

4 Complete the email with the phrases in the box.

after dinner   a good weekend   for a party   in bed
to the cinema   until eleven o'clock   with my brothers

Inbox

Hi Thomas

Great to hear from you! How are things with you?
I had ¹_____ . On Saturday it was my friend
Fiona's birthday. She invited us all ²_____
to see a film. Later, we went to her house ³_____
with food and music. I didn't get home ⁴_____ .
On Sunday I woke up late and read magazines
⁵_____ . Then I got up, listened to music and
played a board game ⁶_____ . I won! I did
my homework ⁷_____ . :-(Luckily it didn't
take long. ;-)
How was your weekend?
Email me soon. Jim says hello.
Love
Patricia

Writing guide

5 Write an email to a friend following the example in exercise 4. You can use activities from exercise 1 to help you.

- Begin your email with a greeting and one or two phrases from exercise 2.
- **First paragraph:** describe what you did on Saturday.
- **Second paragraph:** describe what you did on Sunday.
- Add one or two more phrases from exercise 2.
- Finish your email.

Inbox

_____
_____
_____
_____
_____
_____
_____
_____
_____
_____

CHECK YOUR WORK

Have you:
☐ included phrases from exercise 2?
☐ checked your spelling and grammar?

1 Complete the chart.

Country	Nationality
the USA	1 _____
2 _____	Turkish
Japan	3 _____
4 _____	Brazilian
France	5 _____
6 _____	Irish
Sweden	7 _____
8 _____	Czech

Mark: ____ /8

2 Correct the verbs. Use *make*, *do*, *have* and *take*.

1 Let's **do** lunch now. _____
2 It's sometimes difficult to **take** new friends. _____
3 Do you **make** art at school? _____
4 I often **do** dreams about exams. _____
5 Can you **have** a photo of us with my camera? _____

Mark: ____ /5

3 Complete the sentences. Use the past simple form of the verbs in the box.

| buy   sell   sleep   spend   win   write |

1 I'm not tired. I _____ until eleven o'clock this morning!
2 I _____ my bike on eBay. I got £50 for it.
3 Yesterday evening, Joe _____ a letter to his uncle.
4 Liverpool _____ the match 4–3.
5 We _____ two weeks in France last summer.
6 My parents _____ a new car last weekend.

Mark: ____ /6

4 Complete the first sentence of each pair. Use the past simple negative form of the verb in the second sentence.

1 We _____ at six o'clock. We arrived at five.
2 Tom _____ jeans. He wore trousers.
3 I _____ to London. I went to Manchester.
4 Rachel _____ me an email. She sent me a text.
5 The play _____ at seven o'clock. It began at eight.
6 We _____ our cousins. We visited our grandparents.

Mark: ____ /6

5 Look at the chart. Complete questions for these answers about the things Ann and Mark did at the weekend.

	Saturday	Sunday
Ann		
Mark		

1 What _____ on Saturday?
   She did some housework.
2 _____ computer games on Sunday?
   Yes, he did.
3 When _____ his homework?
   On Saturday.
4 _____ computer games?
   No, she didn't.
5 When _____ her homework?
   On Sunday.

Mark: ____ /5

Total: ____ /30

I can ...

Read the statements. Think about your progress and tick one of the boxes.

★ = I need more practice.   ★★ = I sometimes find this difficult.

★★★ = No problem!

	★	★★	★★★
I can talk about people's countries and nationalities. (SB p.68)			
I can talk about past events. (SB p.69)			
I can understand a text about a historical event. (SB p.70)			
I can say what did and didn't happen in the past. (SB p.71)			
I can understand biographies of famous artists. (SB p.72)			
I can talk about what happened at the weekend. (SB p.74)			
I can write an email describing my weekend. (SB p.75)			

In the wild

8A VOCABULARY Geography

I can talk about geographical places in the world.

1 Look at the pictures and do the crossword.

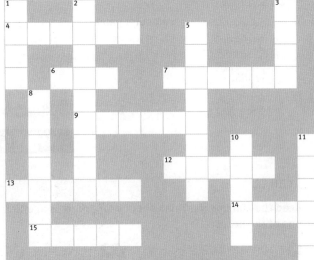

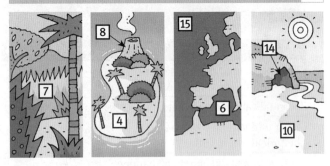

2 Write *The* if necessary, and complete the names of the continents.

1 _The_ Rocky Mountains are in N<u>orth</u> <u>America</u>.
2 _____ Atacama Desert is in S_____ A_____ .
3 _____ Danube River is in E_____ .
4 _____ Lake Manchar is in As_____ .
5 _____ Bondi Beach is in Au_____ .
6 _____ Ross Sea is in An_____ .

3 Label the compass points. Complete the sentences with facts about your country.

1 _____
2 _____
3 _____
4 _____

| east | north | south | west |

1 _____ is in the north of the country.
2 _____ is in the south of the country.
3 _____ is in the east of the country.
4 _____ is in the west of the country.

VOCABULARY BUILDER (PART 2): MEASUREMENTS. >>SB PAGE 138<<

4 Complete the questions with the adjectives in the box.

| big | deep | high | long | old |

1 'How _____ is the Volga river?'
   '3,692 kilometres.'
2 'How _____ is this swimming pool?'
   'One metre at this end and two metres at the other end.'
3 'How _____ is that block of flats?'
   'There are 25 floors.'
4 'How _____ is your house?'
   'It was built in 1873.'
5 'How _____ is the hotel?'
   'There are 300 rooms.'

Challenge!

INTERNET RESEARCH Write four questions about Lake Baikal in Russia. Use *How ...?* and the adjectives in the box. Find the answers online and write them below.

| deep | long | old | wide |

1 _____ ?
   _____
2 _____ ?
   _____
3 _____ ?
   _____
4 _____ ?
   _____

8B **GRAMMAR** Comparative adjectives

I can make comparisons.

1 Read the sentences. Write the correct names of the five boys.

Ewan is taller than Ryan.   Lewis is shorter than Ewan.
Ryan is shorter than Harry.   Jack is shorter than Ryan.
Harry is taller than Ewan.   Lewis is taller than Ryan.

1 _____ 2 _____ 3 _____ 4 _____ 5 _____

2 Complete the table. Use the comparative form of the adjectives in the box.

| attractive bad big famous far fierce funny |
| good heavy hot large rich short tall wide |

+ *er*	
+ *r*	
y → ier	
double consonant + *er*	
more + adj	
irregular	

3 Complete the text. Use the comparative form of the adjectives in brackets.

Humans and chimps: a comparison

Chimpanzees live in the forests of central Africa. They're much ¹ _____ (good) than humans at climbing trees, but on the ground, humans are ² _____ (fast).
Chimps walk on their hands and feet. Their arms are ³ _____ (long) than their legs.

Humans are ⁴ _____ (big) and ⁵ _____ (heavy) than chimps and they're ⁶ _____ (tall) too. But chimps are much ⁷ _____ (strong) than humans. They hunt ⁸ _____ (small) animals for food. Chimps are intelligent animals, but humans are ⁹ _____ (intelligent).

4 Write questions using the words in brackets. Use the comparative form of the adjective. Then answer the questions.

1 (large / an African elephant / an Indian elephant)
  Which is larger, an African elephant or an Indian elephant?
  An African elephant.

2 (intelligent / a chimpanzee / a dog)
  _____
  _____

3 (far from Ireland / Asia / North America)
  _____
  _____

4 (hot / Mexico / Canada)
  _____
  _____

5 (heavy / gold / silver)
  _____
  _____

6 (fattening / fruit / butter)
  _____
  _____

5 Look at the photos and compare the places. Use the comparative form of adjectives from the box, or your own ideas.

| beautiful busy cold exciting hot interesting |

beach

ski resort

The beach is quieter than the ski resort.
_____
_____
_____
_____
_____

I can talk about natural landmarks.

Revision: Student's Book page 80

1 Match the pictures with the outdoor activities in the box.

bird-watching ☐ canoeing ☐ climbing ☐ diving ☐ fishing ☐ horse riding ☐
mountain biking ☐ sailing ☐ skiing ☐ snowboarding ☐ swimming ☐ walking ☐

2 🎧 LISTENING 42 Listen to the information about Mount Fuji. Which two outdoor activities from exercise 1 does it mention?

1 _____ 2 _____

3 🎧 LISTENING 42 Listen again and complete the sentences. Write one word or number in each gap.

1 Mount Fuji is a famous _____ in Japan.

2 Fuji is about _____ kilometres _____ of Tokyo.

3 You can see Fuji in a lot of Japanese _____ .

4 There are five _____ near Mount Fuji.

5 There are a lot of stories about ghosts in the _____ near Fuji.

6 The best months to climb Fuji are _____ and _____ .

7 Climbers usually go up the mountain at _____ .

8 You shouldn't climb Fuji between _____ and May because of the _____ .

4 🎧 LISTENING 43 Listen to Lily talking about a visit to Mount Fuji. Use the questions below to make notes.

When did she visit?	Last August.
Who with?	_____
How did they travel to Fuji?	_____
Where did they have lunch?	_____
What did they do in the afternoon?	_____
How did they travel back to Tokyo?	_____

5 🎧 LISTENING 43 Write a short description of Lily's visit using your notes from exercise 4. Then listen again and check.

_____

_____

_____

_____

_____

_____

Challenge!

Imagine that you visited a famous landmark in your country recently. Write a short description of your visit. Use the questions in exercise 4 to give you ideas.

_____

_____

_____

_____

_____

_____

GRAMMAR Superlative adjectives

I can describe things using superlative adjectives.

1 Put the words in the correct order to make sentences. Tick ✓ the sentences you agree with.

1 funniest / Jack Black / actor / is / in / the / Hollywood

Jack Black _____ . ☐

2 school / at / English / subject / the / difficult / is / most

English _____ . ☐

3 pizza / food / the / is / the / tastiest / world / in

Pizza _____ . ☐

4 is / the / the USA / exciting / most / country / world / the / in

The USA _____ . ☐

5 are / Chelsea / world / in / best / team / football / the / the

Chelsea _____ . ☐

6 worst / exams / about / thing / are / the / school

Exams _____ . ☐

2 Make true sentences from the chart. Use the superlative form of the adjectives.

1 The Amazon		big	animals in the world.
2 The Antarctic		cold	
3 Asia		dangerous	continent in the world.
4 Chimps	is the	far	planet from the sun.
5 Neptune		good	river in the world.
6 Mosquitoes	are the	intelligent	
7 Lionel Messi		noisy	footballer in the world (probably).
8 Howler monkeys		wide	

1 The Amazon is the widest

2 _____

3 _____

4 _____

5 _____

6 _____

7 _____

8 _____

Challenge!

Write five true sentences. Use the superlative form of the adjectives in brackets.

1 (large) _____

2 (hot) _____

3 (fast) _____

4 (expensive) _____

5 (funny) _____

3 Write questions using the prompts. Use the superlative form of the adjectives. Then write your own answers.

1 who / tall / person in your family?

Who is the tallest person in your family?

_____

2 what / good / day of the week?

_____

_____

3 where / expensive / shop in town?

_____

_____

4 what / interesting / show on TV?

_____

_____

4 Underline the mistakes. Rewrite the sentences correctly.

1 Killer whales are fast than sharks. ✗

_____

2 Polar bears are the most largest predators on land. ✗

_____

3 August is the most good month to climb Mount Fuji. ✗

_____

4 Dogs are much uglyer than cats. ✗

_____

5 Antarctica has the worse climate in the world. ✗

_____

5 Complete the email. Use the comparative and superlative forms of the adjectives in brackets.

● ● ●

✉ Inbox

Hi Mario

I'm really looking forward to your visit next month. August is definitely [1]_____ (good) month to come. Are you flying to Heathrow Airport or Gatwick Airport? Gatwick is [2]_____ (far) from my house than Heathrow, but I can come and meet you. We can get the train or the bus to my house. The train is [3]_____ (fast) than the bus, but it's [4]_____ (expensive).

I went to London Zoo last weekend. It isn't [5]_____ (big) zoo in the UK, but it's [6]_____ (old) and probably [7]_____ (famous) too. It wasn't my first visit. When I was [8]_____ (young), I went with my parents. But it's very different now. It's [9]_____ (modern) – and the animals look [10]_____ (happy) too! For me, [11]_____ (interesting) animals were the giant spiders. They're [12]_____ (large) than my hand!

Email me soon!

Dominic

I can understand an article about dangerous animals.

Revision: Student's Book page 82

1 Match the animals with the descriptions.

bat ☐ bear ☐ crocodile ☐ dolphin ☐ eagle ☐
elephant ☐ fly ☐1 hippo ☐ horse ☐ lion ☐
mosquito ☐ rhino ☐ spider ☐ tiger ☐

1 It's a small insect. It lives in every country. It doesn't usually bite or sting.

2 It sleeps in caves in the day. At night, it flies and hunts.

3 It's the biggest of the big cats. It's orange, white and black.

4 It's very intelligent. It lives in the sea, but it isn't a fish.

5 It's the heaviest animal on land.

6 It's the largest reptile. It lives in rivers and is a fierce hunter.

7 It's an insect. It lives in hot places. It bites and it carries diseases.

8 It lives in rivers in Africa. It's big and heavy. It isn't very friendly.

9 It's a large bird. It usually lives in the mountains.

10 It's brown or black. It's got four legs but it can walk on two legs. It usually lives in forests.

11 It's a big cat. It lives in Africa.

12 It lives in Africa and Asia. It's big and grey. It's got a horn on its nose.

13 People ride it.

14 It catches and eats flies.

Challenge!

Choose two more animals. Write descriptions like the ones in exercise 1.

1 Animal: _____
Description: _____
_____

2 Animal: _____
Description: _____
_____

2 Read the text opposite. Which animal is the most dangerous?

_____

3 Match the sentences with animals A–C in the text.

1 They only live in two continents. ☐
2 They're fiercer in the real world than in stories. ☐
3 They live in Africa, America and other continents. ☐
4 They live and hunt in a group. ☐
5 They kill hundreds of people a year. ☐
6 They live in Europe. ☐

Dangerous animals

A Bears

Children love bears. They play with toy bears and read stories about friendly bears. But in fact, bears are very dangerous. They're fierce hunters and they're fast. They can climb trees. You can find bears in North and South America, Europe and Asia. They kill about ten people a year. Imagine you meet a bear in the mountains. What can you do? The best advice is, don't run – bears are faster than humans. Lie on the ground and pretend to be dead.

B Lions

Lions are big cats. They're smaller than tigers, but they're bigger than jaguars and leopards. They live in Africa and in one place in Asia – the Gir Forest in India. They live in family groups and they hunt in pairs or groups. Only female lions hunt, the males don't take part. Lions don't usually hunt humans, but they can. For example, in 1898, two lions killed 135 people in Kenya. So it's a good idea to keep your distance.

C Crocodiles

Crocodiles are the largest reptiles in the world. They live in rivers in hot countries and you can find crocodiles in every continent except Europe and Antarctica. They're very fast in the water – they can swim at 40 km/h – and they can run fast on land too. In Asia and Africa, crocodiles kill more than 500 people a year. The crocodiles hide in the river and then attack suddenly when people are washing or swimming.

I can negotiate plans.

1 Label the types of holiday with the words in the box.

> beach holiday   camping holiday   city break
> climbing holiday   coach tour   cycling holiday
> jungle trek   safari   skiing holiday

1 _____

2 _____

3 _____

4 _____

5 _____

6 _____

7 _____

8 _____

9 _____

2 🎧 **LISTENING 44** Listen to two dialogues. Which holidays from exercise 1 do they talk about? Which do they choose?

Dialogue 1

They talk about going on a _____ and a _____ , but finally decide to go on a _____ .

Dialogue 2

They talk about going on a _____ and a _____ , but finally decide to go on a _____ .

3 🎧 **LISTENING 44** **TRANSLATION** Listen again. Complete the phrases from the dialogues. Then write translations.

1 Why _____ we go on a city break?
_____

2 I don't _____ that's a great idea.
_____

3 How _____ going camping?
_____

4 I think cycling _____ be nicer.
_____

5 I'd _____ to go climbing.
_____

6 That _____ good.
_____

4 Complete the chart with the phrases from exercise 3.

Phrases for negotiating
A Making a suggestion
Shall we (go cycling)?
1
2
Let's (go cycling).
B Raising an objection
3
It's (dangerous). I don't like (cycling). I can't (cycle). Hmm. I don't know. It's (dangerous).
C Suggesting an alternative
4
I'd rather (go climbing).
5
D Agreeing to a suggestion
I agree.
6
OK! That's perfect.

5 Complete the dialogue with appropriate words.

Noah   Where shall we go ¹ _on__ holiday this year?

Isabel   Let's ² _____ on a safari.

Noah   I don't think that's ³ _____ good idea. They're expensive.

Isabel   OK. How ⁴ _____ a jungle trek?

Noah   No thanks. I ⁵ _____ like insects! I'd rather go ⁶ _____ a beach holiday.

Isabel   OK. That sounds good.

Noah   Great! Let's book it today.

6 Write a dialogue like the one in exercise 5. Choose different holidays from exercise 1 and different phrases from exercise 4.

A _____
B _____
A _____

B _____
A _____

B _____
A _____

Preparation

1 Complete the advert with appropriate words.

The black rhino is in danger!

The black rhino lives in Africa. It's one of ¹_____ largest land animals ²_____ the world. It ³_____ got small eyes, and a big horn on its nose. It's called the black rhino, but in fact, it isn't ⁴_____ – it's grey.

In 1970, there were more ⁵_____ 30,000 black rhinos in the wild. Today there are only 3,000. Why ⁶_____ they disappearing? The biggest reason ⁷_____ traditional Chinese medicine. People kill the rhinos and use their horns as an ingredient. Also, people ⁸_____ destroying their habitat.

Help the rhino. Please give £3 ⁹_____ month.

2 Answer the questions about the black rhino.

1 Where do black rhinos live?

_____

2 What colour is a black rhino?

_____

3 How many black rhinos are there in the wild today?

_____

4 Why do people kill black rhinos?

_____

5 What other reason is there for rhinos being in danger?

_____

6 How much money is the advert asking for?

_____

3 Look at the 'Help' message at the end of the advert in exercise 1. Does it include:

a two comparative forms? ☐

b two superlative forms? ☐

c two imperative forms? ☐

4 Rewrite the sentences. Use *so*.

1 I had lunch because I was hungry.

I was <u>hungry so I had lunch</u>_____ .

2 We went out because the weather was nice.

The weather was _____ .

3 Because it was Sunday, I didn't go to school.

It was _____ .

4 You can't hunt tigers because they're in danger.

Tigers are _____ them.

5 You can't go shopping because the shops are closed.

The shops are _____ .

Writing guide

5 Match the questions about giant pandas with the answers in the box.

> About 1,600.   In the forests of China.
> Their habitat is disappearing.   They're black and white bears.

1 Where do giant pandas live?

_____

2 What do giant pandas look like?

_____

3 How many giant pandas are there in the wild today?

_____

4 Why are giant pandas in danger?

_____

6 Write an advert like the one in exercise 1. Use the information from exercise 5 and include a clear 'Help' message at the end. Write 70–90 words.

The _____ is in danger!

_____

_____

_____

_____

_____

_____

_____

_____

CHECK YOUR WORK

Have you:

☐ included all the information in the task in exercise 5?

☐ finished your advert with a clear instruction?

8 Self Check

1 Label each picture with two words from the box.

beach cave forest island lake mountain river sea volcano waterfall

1 a _____ behind a _____
2 a _____ in a _____
3 an _____ in a _____
4 a _____ behind a _____
5 a _____ in the _____

Mark: ___ /10

2 Complete the names of the continents.
1 Portugal, Italy and Sweden are in E_____ .
2 Brazil, Bolivia and Chile are in S_____ A_____ .
3 India, Japan and Thailand are in A_____ .
4 Egypt, Kenya and Somalia are in A_____ .

Mark: ___ /4

3 Put the words in the correct order to make sentences.
1 tall / uncle / how / is / your / ?

_____

2 away / beach / the / two kilometres / is

_____

3 the / deep / swimming pool / two metres / is

_____

4 an / heavy / African / how / is / elephant / ?

_____

Mark: ___ /4

4 Rewrite the sentences. Use the comparative form of the adjective in brackets. Do not change the meaning.
1 Jack is shorter than Martha. (tall)

_____

2 Skodas are cheaper than Porsches. (expensive)

_____

3 Climbing is more dangerous than skiing. (safe)

_____

4 I think Italian food is better than Greek food. (bad)

_____

5 Lions are smaller than polar bears. (big)

_____

Mark: ___ /5

5 Complete the sentences. Use the superlative form of the adjectives in the box.

deep far high hot long popular safe

1 Mount Fuji is the _____ mountain in Japan.
2 The Pacific Ocean is the _____ ocean in the world.
3 The Volga is the _____ river in Europe.
4 The _____ city from Beijing is Buenos Aires.
5 The _____ drink in the world is coffee.
6 The _____ way to travel is by aeroplane.
7 The _____ place in the world is inside a volcano.

Mark: ___ /7

Total: ___ /30

I can ...

Read the statements. Think about your progress and tick one of the boxes.

★ = I need more practice.   ★★ = I sometimes find this difficult.

★★★ = No problem!

	★	★★	★★★
I can talk about geographical places in the world. (SB p.78)			
I can make comparisons. (SB p.79)			
I can talk about natural landmarks. (SB p.80)			
I can describe things using superlative adjectives. (SB p.81)			
I can understand an article about dangerous animals. (SB p.82)			
I can negotiate plans. (SB p.84)			
I can write an advert. (SB p.85)			

EXAM STRATEGY: Reading

- Read the text quickly to get a general idea of what it is about.
- Then read the sentences and the multiple-choice options.
- Read again and underline the relevant information.
- Predict what kind of information is needed in each gap.
- Choose the right option.
- Read the whole text together with the missing sentences.

EXAM TASK – Reading

Read the article about Emmeline Pankhurst. For each gap (1–5) choose the missing sentence (A–G). There are two sentences you do not need.

1 ☐
In her lifetime there were important changes in British society. The day before she died, British women got equal voting rights with men. For the first time, all men and women over the age of 21 could vote for any political party. This was Emmeline's work. She fought for the right of women to vote.

2 ☐
Her parents thought that women and men should be equal. But her parents also believed that women shouldn't work. Emmeline was a clever girl. But her parents didn't send Emmeline to university like her brothers.

3 ☐
He worked in politics and believed in votes for women. But Emmeline also worked in politics and helped women in prison. Richard died in 1898. After he died, Emmeline continued to work in politics, but no one was interested in votes for women. In 1903 she started her own political party – the Women's Social and Political Union (WSPU). Her three daughters helped her, especially her eldest daughter Christabel.

4 ☐
They started to shout at political meetings. They broke the windows of government ministers. For the next nine years Emmeline and her daughters went to prison again and again. British society was shocked by the women, but also by the actions of the police.

5 ☐
This changed everything. Emmeline Pankhurst stopped her fight with the government and told women to go to work. The war ended in 1918, and women over 30 years old got the right to vote. Ten years later, women got equal voting rights with men. British society changed forever and Emmeline Pankhurst became a hero.

A Emmeline met Richard Pankhurst when she was 20 and he was 44.

B Emmeline came from a political family.

C She is a symbol of the fight for equal rights for women at the beginning of the 20th century.

D World War I began in 1914.

E Emmeline Pankhurst was born in England in 1858 and died in 1928 at the age of 69.

F In 1905 the WSPU decided that the government was not listening to their peaceful voices.

G Emmeline began her political career after her marriage.

PREPARATION: Listening

1 Work in pairs. Read the statements in the exam task. Think of different ways of saying them.
2 Read the task again and decide what kind of information you need in each gap (a date, number, place, etc.).

EXAM STRATEGY

- Remember that the recording will often use different words and phrases to say the same ideas as the statements.
- Do not write more than two words in each gap. Sometimes you will need a number.
- Check the grammar in the completed sentences.

EXAM TASK – Listening

🎧 LISTENING 45 Listen to Tom talking about Exmoor National Park in Britain. Complete sentences 1–7 with information from the text. Write only one or two words in each gap.

1 Tom is standing next to a(n) _____ .
2 Tom is planning to travel around the _____ .
3 The paths in Exmoor are more than _____ kilometres long.
4 Tom recommends taking strong walking shoes and _____ with you.
5 Cyclists can join organised _____ in Exmoor.
6 Another sport you can do in Exmoor is _____ .
7 There are many _____ where you can do the sport.

EXAM STRATEGY: Use of English

- Read the whole text first. It will make it easier for you to decide which option is correct.
- All of the options are correct forms, but only one of them fits the meaning and grammar of the sentence.
- Some items test your grammar, others test your vocabulary.
- When you have chosen the answers, read the text again to check.
- Do not leave out any answers. If you are not sure, guess.

EXAM TASK – Use of English

Complete each gap (1–10) with the correct answers (A–D).

Last year I decided to attend 1_____ dancing classes. I did it because I wanted to go out and socialise, and I also 2_____ that I would meet 3_____ nice people there. The school I 4_____ is very popular in our region. I have to say, I learned a lot and I also 5_____ out that dancing can make you very attractive. Girls like guys who can 6_____ and who like 7_____ fun.

To be honest, the dancing was very difficult at times, but I never gave 8_____ because I knew I had to stay focused. Dance has become more important to me 9_____ anything else for various reasons. I believe it is an art which helps you express your feelings and it also 10_____ you good exercise habits and helps you improve your strength and flexibility.

1 A –	B any	C the	D this
2 A hoped	B noticed	C asked	D suggested
3 A much	B any	C some	D the
4 A choose	B was choosing	C chose	D chooses
5 A caught	B moved	C brought	D found
6 A dancing	B dance	C dances	D to dance
7 A have	B had	C having	D has
8 A out	B on	C off	D up
9 A of	B as	C than	D from
10 A teaches	B is teaching	C taught	D teach

EXAM STRATEGY: Writing

- Think about why you are writing the letter. Is it formal or informal?
- Before you start writing the letter, make notes about where you are going, the two attractions, two things to do, and what you will need there.
- Write about each point from the task in a separate paragraph.
- Make sure that you cover all the points in the task and that you have written 160–180 words.

EXAM TASK – Writing

You want to invite an Australian friend to spend a week in the summer camping near an attractive place in your country. In your letter (160–180 words):

- suggest a time and place for the trip
- describe the place and say why it is nice to visit
- suggest two active ways of spending time there
- tell him/her what to bring

PREPARATION: Speaking

1 Write three more phrases in each column below.

Making suggestions	Accepting suggestions	Rejecting suggestions
Why don't we...?	That could be fun!	Well, I'd rather...

2 Read the exam task. Make a few notes about activities, places to eat, places to meet and people to invite.

EXAM STRATEGY

Do not worry; you can invent objections and alternatives. You do not always have to give your real opinion!

EXAM TASK – Speaking

You are planning a day out together with a friend. Discuss the following ideas:

- what you would like to do
- what you would like to eat and where
- where you are going to meet
- other people you would like to invite

You start the conversation.

9A VOCABULARY AND LISTENING | Jobs and work

I can describe different jobs.

1 Circle fifteen more jobs in the wordsearch. Write them below, including *a* or *an*.

L	O	K	E	D	B	U	I	L	D	E	R
S	A	R	T	I	S	T	E	O	O	B	B
M	R	X	E	W	Q	U	A	R	C	P	O
E	C	A	N	G	H	E	R	K	T	R	J
C	H	M	G	U	N	S	T	T	O	O	O
H	I	F	I	L	A	W	Y	E	R	G	U
A	T	L	N	O	C	C	I	A	N	R	R
N	E	L	E	C	T	R	I	C	I	A	N
I	C	M	E	H	I	L	I	H	P	M	A
C	T	U	R	I	A	R	F	E	I	M	L
S	H	S	N	O	E	B	U	R	L	E	I
H	A	I	R	D	R	E	S	S	E	R	S
R	E	C	E	P	T	I	O	N	I	S	T
S	C	I	E	N	T	I	S	T	O	R	M
T	R	A	I	D	E	N	T	M	I	S	S
I	L	N	E	S	O	L	D	I	E	R	D

a builder

_____   _____

_____   _____

_____   _____

_____   _____

_____   _____

_____   _____

_____   _____

2 Solve the puzzles. Write *a* or *an* and jobs from the box.

> actor ~~farmer~~ nurse plumber secretary
> taxi driver vet waiter

1 I usually work outside. I often work with animals. I'm _a farmer_ .

2 I usually work in people's houses. I'm _____ .

3 I often work in theatres. I'm _____ .

4 I usually work inside. I help animals. I'm _____ .

5 I usually work in an office. I'm _____ .

6 I work in a restaurant. I'm _____ .

7 I work in a hospital. I'm _____ .

8 I'm in a car when I'm working. I'm _____ .

3 Who uses these things? Match the pictures with jobs from exercises 1 and 2. Remember to include *a* or *an*.

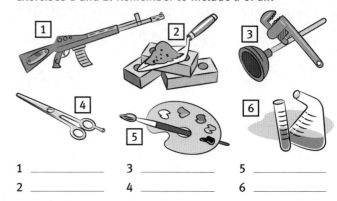

1 _____   3 _____   5 _____

2 _____   4 _____   6 _____

4 🎧 **LISTENING 46** Listen and identify the jobs. Use jobs from exercises 1 and 2. Remember to include *a* or *an*.

Speaker 1 is _____ .

Speaker 2 is _____ .

Speaker 3 is _____ .

Speaker 4 is _____ .

Speaker 5 is _____ .

VOCABULARY BUILDER (PART 2): SUFFIXES: *-ER*, *-OR*, AND *-IST*. ≫SB PAGE 139≪

5 For each verb or noun, write the word for the person who does that activity. All of the words end with *-er*, *-or*, or *-ist*.

1 paint _____   5 sail _____

2 write _____   6 visit _____

3 piano _____   7 cycle _____

4 dance _____   8 therapy _____

Challenge!

Choose three jobs from exercises 1 or 5. Write puzzles like the ones in exercise 2. Ask your partner to solve them.

1 _____
   _____ . I'm _____ .

2 _____
   _____ . I'm _____ .

3 _____
   _____ . I'm _____ .

1 Complete the sentences. Use the affirmative form of *going to* and the verbs in the box.

| cook get ~~leave~~ play surf travel visit watch |

1 I 'm going to leave school early today.
2 My parents _____ a DVD this evening.
3 We _____ volleyball at school next year.
4 My best friend _____ a job next summer.
5 My sister and I _____ dinner this evening.
6 Isobel _____ her grandparents at the weekend.
7 I _____ the Internet after school.
8 My grandparents _____ around the world next year.

2 What are your plans for the weekend? Write true sentences. Use the affirmative or negative form of *going to* and the prompts.

1 do homework
  I'm going to do homework. / I'm not going to do homework.

2 visit family
  _____

3 go shopping
  _____

4 study for an exam
  _____

5 play computer games
  _____

6 tidy my bedroom
  _____

3 🎧 LISTENING 47 Listen to Olivia and Toby talking about their different holiday plans. Tick ✓ or cross ✗ the activities.

	Olivia	Toby and Freya
✈	✓	✗
⛺		
⛱		
🎉		

4 Look again at the chart in exercise 3. Write questions and answers about their holiday plans. Use *going to*.

1 Olivia / travel by plane?
  Is Olivia going to travel by plane?
  Yes, she is.

2 Olivia / stay at a campsite?
  _____
  _____

3 Freya and Toby / stay in a hotel?
  _____
  _____

4 Olivia / go to the beach?
  _____
  _____

5 Freya and Toby / go climbing?
  _____
  _____

5 Complete the messages. Use *going to* and the verbs in brackets.

¹Are you going to be (you / be) at home for the summer holidays?

No, I'm not. I ² _____ (be) in France.

Really? Where ³ _____ (you / stay)?

We ⁴ _____ (not stay) in one place. We ⁵ _____ (spend) two weeks at a campsite. Then we ⁶ _____ (visit) friends. It ⁷ _____ (be) a great summer! What about you?

I ⁸ _____ (work) at my uncle's shop. It ⁹ _____ (not be) a great summer for me.

Challenge!

Write about your plans for the summer holidays. Use *going to*. Use the questions in the box to help you.

What are you going to do?   Where are you going to go?
Who with?   When?   Are you going to work?

_____
_____
_____

CULTURE Jobs for teenagers

I can talk about jobs for young people.

Revision: Student's Book page 90

1 Complete the sentences with the words in the box.

> ambition   career   degree   law   part-time job
> qualifications   ~~skills~~

1 Foreign languages are one of the most useful
   skills you can have.

2 My _____ is to work in the USA.

3 In the UK, it's against the _____ for
   children under fourteen to work.

4 She wants to be a vet, but she needs more
   _____ .

5 He started his _____ in the film industry
   when he was very young.

6 He's got a _____ in physics from
   Harvard University.

7 He's an actor, but he's also got a _____
   in a café.

2 Describe the photo. Where are the people? What are they
wearing? What are they doing? Write 30–40 words.

_____

_____

_____

_____

3 Read the text opposite. Match the photo in exercise 2 with
one of the three part-time jobs: Keira's, Isaac's or Daisy's.

_____'s job is similar to the photo.

4 Match two summary sentences with each person in the text.
Write the names.

1 _____ works for a member of the same family.

2 _____ works with a group of people with a similar age.

3 _____ sells food and drink as part of the job.

4 _____ doesn't think the work is interesting.

5 _____ doesn't work from Monday to Friday.

6 _____ doesn't work with any boys or men.

My part-time job

Keira
I really enjoy my part-time job. I work in my local cinema
four evenings a week. My job is to check people's tickets
at the door and sell drinks and snacks. I enjoy working in
a cinema because I love films. And I like being part of a
team too. We're all about the same age and we often go
out together after work.

Isaac
At weekends, I work at my dad's garage. He's a mechanic.
I haven't got any qualifications so I don't work on the cars
or motorbikes. I answer the phone, I make tea for the
mechanics and I deal with the customers. Next year, I'm
going to do a training course so I can work on the cars too.

Daisy
I work every afternoon after school for two hours at a
factory. It's a food factory – it makes cakes and biscuits.
The work is boring, but it's easy, and I get £7 an hour. The
other workers there are all women. My best friend at work
is from Hungary and she's teaching me Hungarian. I'm
going to visit her home in Hungary next summer.

5 🎧 LISTENING 48 Listen to a conversation about part-
time jobs for teenagers. Tick ✓ the opinions you hear.

a For teenagers, studying is more important than working. ☐

b Working makes teenagers very tired at school. ☐

c It's good for teenagers to get experience of work. ☐

d Companies never pay teenagers very much money. ☐

e You can learn a lot of new skills at work. ☐

f You can meet new people at work. ☐

g You need to get good qualifications to get a good job. ☐

h Teenagers should use their free time for hobbies. ☐

6 🎧 LISTENING 48 Match 1–5 with a–e to make phrases
for expressing opinions. Then listen again and check.

1 I don't think ☐   a with you.

2 That's a ☐   b that's true.

3 I agree with ☐   c true.

4 That's ☐   d you.

5 I don't agree ☐   e good point.

Challenge!

**Is it a good or bad idea for teenagers to work? Why?
Give your own opinion.**

I think it's a _____ idea for teenagers to work

because _____

_____ .

9D **GRAMMAR** *will*

I can talk about the future and make predictions.

1 **Put the words in the correct order to make sentences.**

1 in / Asia / the / World Cup / next / be / will

_____

2 he / remember / won't / name / your

_____

3 English / our / easy / won't / exam / be

_____

4 I / late / tomorrow / for / school / be / won't

_____

5 will / cousins / holiday / be / next / on / month / my

_____

6 we / need / won't / a / today / coat

_____

2 **Write predictions about your own future. Use *will* (affirmative or negative) and the prompts.**

1 live in Europe

I'll live in a city. / I won't live in a city.

2 have children

_____

3 earn a lot of money

_____

4 be a teacher

_____

5 write a novel

_____

6 become famous

_____

Challenge!

Write three more predictions about your own future. Use *I will* or *I won't*. Use the topics below or your own ideas.

career	exams	money	relationships	university

1 _____

_____

2 _____

_____

3 _____

_____

3 **Write questions with *will*. Then write true answers.**

1 you / be / at school / tomorrow?

Will you be at school tomorrow?

Yes, I will. / No, I won't.

2 the Olympic Games / take place / next year?

_____

_____

3 you / have / an exam / next week?

_____

_____

4 tomorrow / be / Friday?

_____

_____

5 you / go / to university / next year?

_____

_____

4 🎧 **LISTENING 49** **Complete the dialogue. Use *will* (affirmative, negative or interrogative) and the verbs in brackets. Then listen and check.**

Halloween party at Tramps

£10 on the door
£6 in advance

Luke Do you want to go to the Halloween party at Tramps this year?

Erin I'm not sure. ¹_____ (we / know) anyone there?

Luke Yes, you ²_____ . Amy and Lola will go. Their uncle works at the night club.

Erin When is it?

Luke Next Friday. It ³_____ (be) a great party, I'm sure. Tickets ⁴_____ (cost) £10 on the night, but we can buy them now for £6.

Erin Oh, but I ⁵_____ (not be) here next Friday. I've got a job interview in London.

Luke Well, the party ⁶_____ (not finish) until late. What time is your train home?

Erin Around five o'clock. I ⁷_____ (get) home at about nine o'clock.

Luke ⁸_____ (you / want) to go out again?

Erin Yes, probably. I ⁹_____ (need) a laugh after my interview!

READING A year out

I can understand an article about gap years.

Gap year adventures

Revision: Student's Book page 92

1 Complete the sentences with a compound noun.
Use one word from box A and one word from box B.

A	B
conservation French part-time ski tourist ~~voluntary~~	Alps industry instructor jobs project ~~work~~

1 I'm going to do voluntary   work   in a children's hospital in Brazil.

2 She's going on a skiing holiday in the _____ .

3 A lot of British teenagers do _____ _____ to earn money.

4 My sister got married to a _____ _____ .

5 The country makes most of its money from the _____ _____ .

6 There's a _____ _____ to help protect the rainforest.

2 Complete the text opposite with the verbs in the box.

do earn get give lead take learn

3 Match the photos opposite with two of the three parts of the text. Write the names.

Photo 1: _____
Photo 2: _____

4 Read the text again. Are the sentences true (T) or false (F)?

1 Lily is going to travel alone. ☐
2 Lily will probably take another year off after university. ☐
3 Evan wants a career in IT after university. ☐
4 Evan's training course is two months long. ☐
5 Abigail will earn a lot of money in Senegal. ☐
6 Abigail doesn't know what she wants to do after university. ☐

5 Choose one person from the text. Write a short summary (20–30 words) in your own language of his or her plans.

_____
_____
_____
_____
_____
_____

When I leave school, I really want to ¹_____ a year off and travel. In four years' time, when I finish my degree, I'll probably start a job immediately because I'll need to ²_____ money. So the best time to travel is before university. My best friend wants to do the same thing. We'll start in France and then we'll go east through Germany and Poland. After that, who knows? **Lily**

I'm going to spend a year working when I leave school. It isn't just because I need money for the fees. I also want to ³_____ experience. My ambition is to be a programmer, so I'll look for jobs at IT companies. But first, I'm going to ⁴_____ a training course in programming. It will take two months and will help me to get a better job. **Evan**

My hobby is sport, and in my year off, I'm going to do voluntary work in Senegal. I'm going to ⁵_____ a team of sports teachers and we're all going to ⁶_____ lessons in different primary schools in the region. I think I'll really enjoy it. And I'll ⁷_____ a new language too! It will be good experience, because I want to be a sports teacher when I leave university. **Abigail**

Challenge!

Imagine you are going to work during a gap year. Write a short text about your plans. Decide:

• the place of work and the job
• why you want to do that job

_____
_____
_____
_____

On the phone

I can make a phone call and leave a message.

1 Look at the pictures and complete the offers. Use *I'll* and the verbs in the box.

give   help   open   phone   repair   turn

1 _____ the door.

2 _____ the music down.

3 _____ you a ride on my motorbike.

4 _____ you find your hotel.

5 _____ the zoo.

6 _____ your skateboard.

2 🎧 **LISTENING 50** Listen and circle the mistake in each phone number. Write the numbers correctly.

1 07737 871100

_____

2 0207 4768251

_____

3 055537 100660

_____

4 01754 888410

_____

5 01566 233409

_____

6 0207 654 3322

_____

3 🎧 **LISTENING 51** Listen and choose the options you hear.

Brooke Hello. Can I help you?

Tyler Oh, hello. ¹**It's / This is** Tyler Wallace here. I'd like to speak to Robin Hanson.

Brooke I'm afraid Mr Hanson isn't ²**available / here** at the moment. ³**Would you like to leave / Can I take** a message?

Tyler Yes. Please could you ask him to ⁴**call me / give me a call**?

Brooke Yes, of course. Can I take your number?

Tyler Yes. It's 01652 876986.

Brooke Thanks for ⁵**your call / calling**. I'll ⁶**make sure he gets / give him** the message.

Tyler Thank you. Goodbye.

4 Complete the dialogue. Use the phrases in the box.

Can I leave   Can I speak   Can you ask her
I'm afraid she's on the phone   I'll try her

Brooke Hello. Can I help you?

Joel Oh, hi. ¹_____ to Lucy Vincent, please?

Brooke One moment, please. ²_____ for you.

Joel Thanks.

Brooke ³_____ at the moment.

Joel Oh, OK. ⁴_____ a message?

Brooke Yes, of course.

Joel ⁵_____ to give me a call? My number is 01435 775351.

Brooke Certainly.

Joel Thank you. Goodbye.

5 Write a dialogue like the one in exercise 4. Invent the name of the person you want to speak to.

Brooke Hello. Can I help you?

You _____

Brooke _____

You _____

Brooke _____

You _____

Brooke _____

You _____

Brooke _____

You Thank you. Goodbye.

I can write a letter applying for a job.

Preparation

1 Complete the letter. Choose from options a–d below.

> Dear Sir or Madam,
>
> I am ¹_____ to apply for a part-time job ²_____ a receptionist at your hotel. I read about the vacancy ³_____ .
>
> I am nineteen years old, and I am in my first year at university. Last summer, I worked at a sports centre for six weeks, so I have experience of ⁴_____ with the public.
>
> I am very interested in this job because I want to work in the tourist ⁵_____ when I leave university. I believe I have the right qualities for the job: I am reliable, honest and polite.
>
> I am ⁶_____ my CV with this letter, and also contact details of two referees. I am available to start work immediately.
>
> I hope to hear from you soon.
>
> Yours faithfully,
>
> *L C Wainwright*
>
> Lucas Wainwright

	a	b	c	d
1	a write	b contacting	c writing	d letter
2	a as	b of	c in	d for
3	a Internet	b advert	c newspaper	d online
4	a meeting	b meet	c dealing	d deal
5	a industry	b job	c company	d team
6	a putting	b enclosing	c offering	d closing

2 Which sentences are too informal for a formal letter? Rewrite them in a more formal style. Tick ✓ the ones that are already formal.

1 I would like to apply for a job in your shop. ☐

_____

2 I know lots about dealing with the public. ☐

_____

3 I can start work whenever you like. ☐

_____

4 Here's my CV and a reference. ☐

_____

5 Hear from you soon, I hope. ☐

_____

6 I saw your advertisement in the local newspaper. ☐

_____

3 Read the online job advert. Underline any information you will need for an application letter.

> # Part-time jobs at **House of York**
>
> We are looking for part-time workers at our department store in Leeds. You must be hard-working and reliable. No qualifications are necessary, but experience of dealing with the public will be an advantage.

Writing guide

4 Write a letter (90–110 words) applying for the job in exercise 3. Include the information below.

- what job you are applying for and where you saw the advertisement
- your age and some basic information about yourself
- your reason for wanting the job and your relevant experience or qualifications
- what you are enclosing with the letter and when you can start

> Dear Sir or Madam,
>
> _____
> _____
> _____
> _____
> _____
> _____
> _____
> _____
> _____
> _____
> _____
> _____
>
> Yours _____ ,
> [your name] _____

CHECK YOUR WORK

Have you:
- ☐ included all the information in the task in exercise 4?
- ☐ avoided language that is too informal?
- ☐ checked your spelling and grammar?

1 Label the pictures with the jobs in the box.

| architect | builder | electrician | engineer | hairdresser |
| scientist | soldier | waiter |

1 an _____ 2 a _____ 3 a _____

4 an _____ 5 a _____ 6 a _____

7 a _____ 8 an _____

Mark: ___ /8

2 Complete the words with the correct suffix: -or, -er, or -ist.

1 sail_____   3 direct_____
2 guitar_____   4 manag_____

Mark: ___ /4

3 Circle a mistake in each sentence. Write the correct words.

1 I not going to be at school tomorrow. _____
2 You aren't going study this weekend. _____
3 My mum and dad is going to stay at home. _____
4 We not are going to have a holiday this year. _____

Mark: ___ /4

4 Complete the questions and short answers. Use going to.

1 _____ Mason and his family _____ have a holiday next month?
Yes, _____ .
2 _____ Mason _____ send any postcards?
No, _____ .
3 _____ his dad _____ take his laptop?
Yes, _____ .
4 _____ Mason and his brother _____ share a room?
No, _____ .

Mark: ___ /4

5 Complete the sentences. Use will or won't and the verbs in the box. Use the short form of will where possible.

| not be | earn | enjoy | finish | not need |

1 We _____ a car when we move to London.
2 Next year, my brother _____ more money than my dad.
3 The theatre _____ open until next month.
4 My sister _____ her degree next year.
5 You _____ the show – it's a great musical.

Mark: ___ /5

6 Complete the dialogue. Use the correct form of will and short answers.

Boy Bye, Mum. I'm going to the cinema. See you later!
Mum What time [1]_____ (you / be) home?
[2]_____ (you / be) very late?
Boy No, [3]_____ . The film finishes at ten.
Mum [4]_____ (you / walk) home?
Boy Yes, [5]_____ . But I'll be with my friends.

Mark: ___ /5

Total: ___ /30

I can ...

Read the statements. Think about your progress and tick one of the boxes.

✱ = I need more practice.   ✱✱ = I sometimes find this difficult.
✱✱✱ = No problem!

	✱	✱✱	✱✱✱
I can describe different jobs. (SB p.88)			
I can talk about my plans for the future. (SB p.89)			
I can talk about jobs for young people. (SB p.90)			
I can talk about the future and make predictions. (SB p.91)			
I can understand an article about gap years. (SB p.92)			
I can make a phone call and leave a message. (SB p.94)			
I can write a letter applying for a job. (SB p.95)			

10 Time to travel

10A VOCABULARY Transport

I can talk about different types of transport.

1 Write the transport words. Match them with pictures a–p.

1	aintr	train	k
2	sub	___	☐
3	timkboore	___	☐
4	cileporhet	___	☐
5	avn	___	☐
6	obat	___	☐
7	chaoc	___	☐
8	lapne	___	☐
9	arc	___	☐
10	pish	___	☐
11	ramt	___	☐
12	kibe	___	☐
13	costoer	___	☐
14	xati	___	☐
15	rylor	___	☐
16	grodunredun ratin	___	☐

2 Rewrite the sentences. Use the words in brackets.

1 We drove to London. (by car)
   We went to London by car.

2 Wendy went to the airport by taxi. (took)
   _____

3 Do you cycle to school? (bike)
   _____

4 Sam gave me a lift to the station. (drove)
   _____

5 I sometimes walk to school. (on foot)
   _____

6 Mum took the tram to town. (by tram)
   _____

3 Complete the adjectives to describe transport with *a, e, i, o* and *u*. Then match 1–5 with the opposite meanings a–e.

1 s __ f __   ☐   a f __ st
2 c __ mf __ rt __ bl __   ☐   b __ nc __ nv __ n __ __ __ nt
3 sl __ w   ☐   c __ nc __ mf __ rt __ bl __
4 ch __ __ p   ☐   d d __ ng __ r __ __ s
5 c __ nv __ n __ __ nt   ☐   e __ xp __ ns __ v __

VOCABULARY BUILDER (PART 2): PHRASAL VERBS. >>SB PAGE 140<<

4 Complete the sentences with the words in the box. You can use some words more than once.

> down   in   off   on   out

1 Sorry we're late. The car broke _____ on the way here.

2 Our plane took _____ at 10.00 and arrived two hours later.

3 The driver got _____ of his lorry and went into the café.

4 The tram stopped and everybody got _____ .

5 Buy a ticket from the driver when you get _____ the bus.

6 Slow _____ ! You're going too fast!

7 We're going now, everyone. Get _____ the car.

Challenge!

DICTIONARY WORK Check the meaning of these words in a dictionary. Then write a sentence with each word.

> departure lounge   motorway   passenger   platform   port   timetable

1 _____
2 _____
3 _____
4 _____
5 _____
6 _____

GRAMMAR Present perfect affirmative

I can say what has just happened.

1 Complete the table. Use the past simple and past participle forms of the verbs.

	past simple	past participle
1 study		
2 use		
3 know		
4 watch		
5 plan		
6 speak		

2 Write sentences. Use the present perfect affirmative.

1 Charles / move / to London

_____

2 Mum / cook / dinner

_____

3 Henry and Sally / sell / their house

_____

4 We / invite / 50 people to our party

_____

5 Becky / grow / four centimetres taller this year

_____

3 Ben and Libby are going to Ireland on holiday. Complete the story. Use the present perfect form of the verb in brackets.

4 Complete the sentences. Use the present perfect affirmative with *just*.

1 'Why are you laughing?'
   'I *have just heard* a funny story.' (hear)

2 'Are you thirsty?'
   'No, I _____ a drink.' (have)

3 'Is Paula here yet?'
   'Yes, she _____ . She's in the hall.' (arrive)

4 'Where's Fred?'
   'He _____ to town. He left a few minutes ago.' (go)

5 'Have you invited Liam to your party?'
   'Yes, I _____ him a text.' (send)

6 'Is it still snowing?'
   'No, it _____ .' (stop)

Challenge!

Complete the sentences with your own ideas. Use the present perfect.

1 Sue is thirsty because _____
   _____.

2 Tom is angry because _____
   _____.

3 Mike is happy because _____
   _____.

They ¹_____ (pack) their suitcases.

They ²_____ (catch) a bus to the airport, but it ³_____ (stop).

Sorry, the bus ⁴_____ (break down).

Their plane ⁵_____ (just / take off).

Oh, no. We ⁶_____ (miss) our plane.

24 hours later ... The plane ⁷_____ (land) in Dublin.

Can I see your passports, please?

Sorry, I ⁸_____ (drop) my bag.

It ⁹_____ (begin) to rain.

Oh, no. I ¹⁰_____ (leave) my coat at home!

They ¹¹_____ (get) to the hotel.

We ¹²_____ (reserve) a room.

Sorry. I can't find it.

Revision: Student's Book page 100

1 Complete the sentences with the words in the box.

> crowded   enormous   sick   successful   tiny   tiring

1 My dad was _____ last week, so he didn't go to work.
2 Babies have got _____ fingers and toes.
3 The Pacific Ocean is _____ – it's over 165,000,000 km².
4 There were 50 people in a small room – it was very _____ .
5 The flight to Australia took 24 hours. It was a very _____ journey.
6 She's a rich and _____ businesswoman.

2 Read the text and answer the questions. Ignore the gaps.

1 How did the Aboriginal people get to Australia?

_____

2 When did Australia become British?

_____

3 Why did Britain stop sending prisoners to America?

_____

3 Read the text again. Match sentences A–F with gaps 1–5. There is one sentence that you do not need.

A He named it New South Wales.
B Farm land was cheap in this big country.
C They left Britain to look for a better life abroad.
D When Australia became a separate country, the Aboriginal people were on their own for a long time.
E When they arrived, they couldn't find work.
F British prisoners went to Australia for the next 50 years.

AUSTRALIA

Australia is an enormous country, but it has been almost empty of people for most of its history. The Aboriginal people walked there from Asia over 50,000 years ago when the two continents were joined by land. ¹_____

The first explorers from Europe arrived in the 17ᵗʰ century, but they didn't stay. Then, in 1770, Captain Cook landed on the east coast of Australia, and it became British. ²_____ Seventeen years later, the first British immigrants arrived to start a new life there. They were mostly British prisoners! Before 1776, Britain sent prisoners to North America, but America was now independent, so Britain couldn't send prisoners there any more. ³_____ The place where they lived is now the city of Sydney.

4 🎧 LISTENING 52 Listen to an Australian woman talking about her ancestors. Does she find out more about:

☐ her ancestors?   ☐ her husband's ancestors?

5 🎧 LISTENING 52 Listen again. Choose the correct answers.

1 Shelley wanted to find out about her family history because
  a she likes Australian history.   b she's got children.
  c she's a descendant of British prisoners.
2 Shelley found out that her family were
  a British.   b prisoners.   c from London.
3 Shelley's husband's great-great-great-great grandparents
  a were both thieves.   b lived in Sydney.
  c arrived in Australia in 1826.
4 John Bullen
  a didn't have a home in England.
  b was fourteen when he went to Australia.
  c wanted to go to Australia.

Challenge!

Write a few sentences about your ancestors.

• What did they do?
• Where did they live?
• Other interesting information about them?

_____
_____
_____
_____
_____

Many other British people sailed to this new country too. ⁴_____ The sea journey was long and difficult – it took eight months, and many people died on the ships. But thousands arrived in Australia to become farmers. ⁵_____ Life wasn't easy, but the new immigrants worked hard and made Australia successful.

GRAMMAR Present perfect negative and interrogative

I can talk about recent events.

1 **Make the sentences negative.**

1 Luke has sent a postcard to his cousin.
   Luke hasn't sent a postcard to his cousin.

2 I've done the washing-up.

3 We've bought a car.

4 They've had lunch.

5 You've tidied your bedroom.

6 It's stopped raining.

2 **Write replies with the present perfect affirmative and *already*.**

1 Do your homework!
   I've already done it.

2 Can you phone Joanna?

3 Why don't you buy the new Adele CD?

4 When are you going to have breakfast?

5 Please tidy your room.

6 Can you change the holiday money?

3 🎧 **LISTENING 53** Toby Church and Lucy Hart are going to drive across the Sahara Desert. Listen to their conversation. Tick ✓ the things they have done.

Things to do

1 *fill bottles with water* ☐
2 *pack food* ☐
3 *buy map and compass* ☐
4 *check car* ☐
5 *look at weather report* ☐
6 *phone parents* ☐
7 *send text messages to friends* ☐

4 **Write questions and answers about 1–7 in exercise 3. Use the present perfect and *yet*.**

1 Have they filled the bottles with water yet?
   No, they haven't.

2

3

4

5

6

7

5 **Write sentences and questions. Use the present perfect and the words in brackets.**

1 you / buy / a guidebook? (yet)
   Have you bought a guidebook yet?

2 I / write / some postcards (already)

3 he / not walk / along the River Thames (yet)

4 she / see / the Queen? (yet)

5 we / take / a coach tour (already)

6 you / visit / Buckingham Palace? (yet)

7 we / not find / our passports (yet)

8 you / spend / a day / on the beach (already)

Challenge!

Write three things that you have already done today and three things that you have not done yet. Use the present perfect with *already* and *yet*.

1
2
3
4
5
6

1 Choose the correct time expressions. Sometimes two answers are possible.

1 **Nowadays / Suddenly / Then**, a lot of people visit Australia.

2 My brother failed his driving test three times. But **finally / eventually / nowadays** he passed it.

3 **Suddenly / Nowadays / Finally**, Helen left the room.

4 I've **recently / finally / afterwards** learned how to swim.

5 **First of all / Finally / Then**, we visited Spain, **then / afterwards / recently** we went to France.

2 Complete the text with the adjectives in the box.

big   dark   deep   happy   hot   hungry   quiet
terrible   worried

In the Outback

IN 2008, my friend Andy and I were on holiday in the Outback in Western Australia. It's a ¹ _big_ place and there aren't many people. We had a car, and every day we drove to the next roadhouse. A roadhouse is like a garage and a shop in the middle of nowhere. We stopped every afternoon to hike in the canyons. The weather was very ² _____ , but we had enough food and water for two days and a radio phone for emergencies. It was an adventure!

But one evening everything changed. We were in our sleeping bags in the car. Suddenly, we heard a strange sound. It was ³ _____ , and we couldn't see anything. It became really windy. Then there was a ⁴ _____ noise and something hit us. It was a tornado! The car lifted off the ground. After that, it was very calm and ⁵ _____ . But we didn't sleep again that night; we were so scared.

In the morning, we saw ⁶ _____ water all around the car. The road was flooded because of the tornado. We couldn't move, but we weren't ⁷ _____ because we had the emergency phone. Finally, we spoke to someone. He told us to wait in the car. We waited four days until a helicopter rescued us. We became quite ⁸ _____ and thirsty, but we were OK – and very ⁹ _____ to see our rescuers. It wasn't an adventure any more!

3 Read the text again. Number the events in the correct order.

a ☐ The tornado moved the car.

b ☐ They were asleep in the car.

c ☐ They went on holiday to Western Australia.

d ☐ The helicopter arrived.

e ☐ The flood waters arrived.

f ☐ They finished all the food and drink in the car.

g ☐ They heard a loud noise.

h ☐ They phoned the emergency services.

Challenge!

INTERNET RESEARCH Find out about Australia. Complete the table.

Population:	
Capital:	
Biggest city:	
Tallest mountain:	
Animals that only live in Australia:	
Another interesting fact:	

EVERYDAY ENGLISH Buying a train ticket

I can buy a train ticket.

1 DICTIONARY WORK Match the words with the definitions.

change (verb)   direct train   platform   railcard
return ticket   single ticket

definition a ticket for a journey to a place and back again

1 _____

definition the place where you get on and off trains at a station

2 _____

definition to get off one train and get on another to complete your journey

3 _____

definition a ticket for a journey to a place, but not back again

4 _____

definition a train that goes all the way to a place

5 _____

definition a special card that lets you travel on trains for a lower price

6 _____

2 LISTENING 54 Listen and write the times.

a __ __.__ __   d __ __.__ __   g __ __.__ __
b __ __.__ __   e __ __.__ __   h __ __.__ __
c __ __.__ __   f __ __.__ __

3 Write the train times in words.

1 06.45   *six forty-five* _____
2 15.00 _____
3 10.55 _____
4 19.08 _____
5 23.15 _____
6 07.39 _____
7 08.00 _____
8 12.33 _____

4 LISTENING 55 Listen to the dialogue. Choose the correct answers.

1 The girl wants a **single / return** ticket.
2 She **has got / hasn't got** a railcard.
3 The ticket costs **£21 / £25**.
4 The next train is at **10.42 / 11.42**.
5 She **has to / doesn't have to** change.

5 Put the words in the correct order to make sentences and questions.

a does / which / leave / it / from? / platform
_____

b a / is / direct / it / train?
_____

c the / 15.26 / train / is / next / at
_____

d to / return ticket / I'd / please / London, / like / a
_____

e you / when / coming / back? / are
_____

f please. / £93, / that's
_____

6 LISTENING 56 Complete the dialogue with lines a–f from exercise 5. Then listen and check.

Clerk   Next please.
Chris   ¹___
Clerk   ²___
Chris   Next Monday.
Clerk   ³___
Chris   Here you are.
Clerk   Thank you. And £7 change.
Chris   ⁴___
Clerk   Number three. ⁵___
Chris   ⁶___
Clerk   No, you have to change at Exeter.

17.44 GLASGOW DIRECT PLATFORM 6

7 Write a dialogue like the one in exercise 6. Use the information on the departure board.

Clerk   _____
Louise Hello. I'd like a return ticket to Glasgow, please.
Clerk   _____ ?
Louise Tomorrow.
Clerk   That's £47, please.
Louise _____
Clerk   _____ . And £3 change.
Louise _____ ?
Clerk   _____
Louise _____ ?
Clerk   _____

10G WRITING A postcard

I can write a postcard about my holiday.

Preparation

1 Label the pictures with the words in the box.

| apartment   campsite   hotel   villa   youth hostel |

1 _____

2 _____

3 _____

4 _____

5 _____

2 Put the words in the correct order to make useful phrases for postcards.

1 on / in / holiday / Croatia. / we're
_____

2 is / this / in / our / day / Italy. / second
_____

3 horrible. / hostel / youth / is / the
_____

4 really / at / cold / moment. / it's / the
_____

5 you / wish / here! / were
_____

6 hello / say / brother! / to / your
_____

3 TRANSLATION Translate the sentences in exercise 2.

1 _____
2 _____
3 _____
4 _____
5 _____
6 _____

4 Complete the postcard. Use the present continuous, past simple and present perfect form of the verbs in brackets.

> Dear Marianne,
> We ¹ 're spending _____ (spend) a week in Scotland.
> We ² _____ (stay) at a small campsite near Edinburgh. The campsite is horrible, but we're
> ³ _____ (enjoy) the lovely weather!
> Yesterday morning, we ⁴ _____ (go) to Princes Street and ⁵ _____ (do) some shopping. I ⁶ _____ (buy) a pair of jeans.
> We ⁷ _____ (not visit) the castle yet.
> We ⁸ _____ (go) there tomorrow.
> Wish you were here!
> Bye for now,
> Ann x

Writing guide

5 Imagine you are on holiday. Make notes about the holiday.

Where?	
Accommodation:	
Weather:	
Two things you did:	
Something you haven't done yet:	

6 Write a postcard like the one in exercise 4. Use your notes from exercise 5.

_____
_____
_____
_____
_____
_____
_____
_____
_____

CHECK YOUR WORK

Have you:
- [ ] included useful phrases from exercise 2?
- [ ] included all the information in the task in exercise 5?
- [ ] checked your spelling and grammar?

1 Label the pictures.

1 _____ 2 _____ 3 _____

4 _____ 5 _____ 6 _____

Mark: ___ /6

2 Match 1–4 with a–d to make adjectives that describe means of transport.

1 comfort ☐   a ient
2 conven ☐   b ive
3 danger ☐   c able
4 expens ☐   d ous

Mark: ___ /4

3 Choose the correct words.

1 Our car broke **down** / **off** / **back** last weekend.
2 Please get **off** / **out of** / **down** the taxi.
3 You're driving too fast. Slow **back** / **off** / **down**!
4 The plane took **off** / **back** / **up** from the airport.
5 What time did you go **off** / **back** / **out** last night?

Mark: ___ /5

4 Complete the sentences. Use the present perfect form of the verbs in the box, and *just*.

| arrive | buy | finish | leave | start |

1 Oh dear. It _____ to rain.
2 Look at my new scooter. I _____ it.
3 Kate isn't here. She _____ .
4 Dan _____ . He's in the kitchen.
5 'Why is Adam so happy?' 'He _____ his exams.'

Mark: ___ /5

5 Look at Jason's list and write five sentences. Use the present perfect, affirmative or negative, with *already* or *yet*.

1 He _____
2 _____
3 _____
4 _____
5 _____

tidy my bedroom ✗
do my homework ✓
help with the cooking ✗
practise the guitar ✓
phone Max ✗

Mark: ___ /5

6 Complete the questions and short answers. Use the present perfect form of the verbs in brackets.

1 '_____ Millie _____ her suitcase yet?' (pack)
'Yes, _____ .'
2 '_____ Harry and Daisy _____ their passports?' (find)
'No, _____ .'
3 '_____ you _____ the tickets, Tom?' (buy)
'Yes, _____ .'
4 '_____ Jason _____ the luggage labels?' (write)
'No, _____ .'
5 '_____ you and Joanna _____ some money?' (change)
'Yes, _____ .'

Mark: ___ /5

Total: ___ /30

I can …

Read the statements. Think about your progress and tick one of the boxes.

★ = I need more practice.   ★★ = I sometimes find this difficult.

★★★ = No problem!

	★	★★	★★★
I can talk about different types of transport. (SB p.98)			
I can say what has just happened. (SB p.99)			
I can talk about immigration. (SB p.100)			
I can talk about recent events. (SB p.101)			
I can understand a newspaper article. (SB p.102)			
I can buy a train ticket. (SB p.104)			
I can write a postcard about my holiday. (SB p.105)			

PREPARATION: Listening

1 Read the task and the sentences. What is the topic?
2 Work in pairs. Think of different ways of saying each question.

EXAM STRATEGY

- Read the task and the sentences. Underline key words.
- During the first listening, listen out for words and expressions that relate to the words that you underlined.
- As you listen, match the questions to the speakers that you're already sure of.
- Listen again and complete all your answers.

EXAM TASK – Listening

🎧 LISTENING 57 Listen to five people talking about their travel experiences. Match each question (A–F) to one of the speakers (1–5). There is one question you do not need.

Which speaker:

A did not enjoy the sea journey? _____
B uses an environmentally-friendly means of transport? _____
C felt like an adult during the journey? _____
D thinks that their journey was exciting, although not always safe? _____
E usually travels with another person? _____
F is not very keen on flying? _____

PREPARATION: Reading

1 Read the task and answer the questions.
  a How many emails are in the text?
  b How many missing phrases are there?
2 Read the text to get a general understanding. Give a short summary of what each person says.

EXAM STRATEGY

- Read the text, ignoring the gaps, to find out what it is about.
- Read the text before and after the gap carefully and think about the grammar and the meaning of the text.
- Always read all the phrases in the list.
- Repeat the process for each gap.

EXAM TASK – Reading

Read some emails in which people talk about their jobs. Some phrases have been removed from the text. For each gap (1–6) choose the correct missing phrase (A–I). You can only use each phrase once. There are three phrases you do not need.

Odd jobs
We are asking you, the public, to help us make a television programme about careers.
Do you have an unusual job? Is it interesting, boring, safe, dangerous, clean or dirty? We want to hear your story. Please email us.

Lesley-Ann
I'm a driving instructor for a fire brigade. I come from a family of lorry drivers and I drove trucks for ten years. I love my job. It's great to watch new drivers with the fire engines – they say [1]_____ . That's important for someone in my position. I think there should be more female fire engine drivers.

Nick
I work as a board games tester with ten other people. I only do this job once a year, for a few months before Christmas, [2]_____ . I normally work in a library. We test all the new games [3]_____ . Our job is to play the games until they break!

Fiona
I work for a large university. It is my job to look after 1,250 student bedrooms and [4]_____ . If you've got teenage children at home, you'll probably have an idea of the problems I face! You have [5]_____ and also laugh!

Mike
I worked for many years in a small chocolate factory. We made chocolate into all kinds of shapes. If people asked us to design a shape for a special occasion, [6]_____ . We were especially busy in the months before Christmas, of course. And yes, I still love chocolate!

A to do an artistic job there
B before they go into the shops
C to be very patient with them
D keep them clean
E but I love it
F we did it
G before he asks other people to help
H to do it well
I I'm very patient

EXAM STRATEGY: Use of English

To be sure your answer is correct, make sure the other options are wrong.

EXAM TASK – Use of English

Complete each gap (1–10) with the correct answer (A–D).

Before I go to university, I ¹_____ in the UK for a year. I'm leaving next month. I've ²_____ found a job: I'm going to be an au pair for a family in London. I ³_____ to London but I'm looking forward ⁴_____ it. I'm going to live near Gatwick Airport. The family has got two children; two little girls. The father is a pilot – he flies planes to the USA – and the mother is a musician. They ⁵_____ travel a lot so I'll look after the girls on my own while they are away. I'm nervous about ⁶_____ the family car because they drive on the left in the UK, but hopefully I'll be okay. I also think I'll get lost on the Underground – it's so big! My friend Peter ⁷_____ in London for a year. He's a messenger and ⁸_____ a motorbike. He says he's going ⁹_____ me to Brighton. He thinks I'll love it there because it's by the seaside. It's only 45 minutes by train. I'm going to ¹⁰_____ a blog when I'm there, and when I get back I'm going to university to train to become a journalist.

1 A 'll live   B 'm going to live   C 'm living   D live
2 A yet   B already   C still   D always
3 A 've never been   B didn't go
   C haven't gone   D never went
4 A at   B on   C of   D to
5 A all   B two   C both   D the two
6 A driving   B riding   C going   D doing
7 A lived   B has lived   C lives   D is living
8 A drives   B goes   C takes   D rides
9 A take   B took   C to take   D taking
10 A make   B write   C take   D use

PREPARATION: Writing

1 Read the task. What is the purpose of the letter? Is it formal or informal?
2 Plan your letter carefully. Make brief notes below covering all the points in the task.

EXAM STRATEGY

Set phrases are very important in formal letters. You have to learn them. See the Writing Bank on page 110.

EXAM TASK – Writing

You have found a job advertisement for a holiday tour guide. Write a letter of application (160–180 words) for the job. Include information on the following:

- where and when you found the advertisement
- your skills and qualifications
- your experience and why you think you are a good candidate for the post
- when you can start work and what you are enclosing with the letter

PREPARATION: Speaking

1 Look at the pictures and answer these questions:
   a Who can you see in the pictures?
   b Where are they and what are they doing?
   c How do you feel about the atmosphere in the pictures?

EXAM STRATEGY

- Read the task. Think about the vocabulary you will need to describe, compare and contrast the photos.
- Think about what the pictures have in common and how they are different.

EXAM TASK – Speaking

Compare and contrast the pictures and say what you think about these two jobs. Include the following information:

- What do a vet and a doctor have in common?
- What are the positive and negative aspects of each job?
- What skills or training do you need to do each job?
- Would you like to be a vet or a doctor? Why? / Why not?

1 Complete the text with appropriate words.

The sport of ice dancing is part ¹_____ the Winter Olympics. The rules of ice dancing are different from ordinary skating competitions. ²_____ example, in ice dancing, the skaters can't do big jumps or spins. And an important part of ice dancing ³_____ choosing the music and creating the dance.

In ⁴_____ UK, *Dancing on Ice* is a very popular ⁵_____ programme. It's about an ice dancing competition. Celebrities and professional skaters ⁶_____ part together in pairs. Each week, the pairs learn a new dance. People ⁷_____ home vote for their favourites and each week, one pair leaves the competition. Ice dancing ⁸_____ a new sport – it's about a hundred years old – but because ⁹_____ *Dancing on Ice*, it's now ¹⁰_____ very popular hobby.

Mark: ____ /10

2 Complete the email with the words in the box.

badly   chat   great   hardly   interested   often   old   parents   quite   same   sisters   soon   visit   wishes

Inbox

Dear Anna,

Hi! I'm Libby and I'm 17 years ¹_____ . I like your message on the Student Exchange Forum. Your English is ²_____ !

I live in South London with my ³_____ and my grandma. I haven't got brothers or ⁴_____ , but I've got lots of cousins. Five of my cousins live in London, so I ⁵_____ see them.

My hobbies aren't exactly the ⁶_____ as your hobbies, but that's OK. I'm ⁷_____ in sport – I like football and tennis. I like basketball too, but I ⁸_____ ever play it. I love films and I ⁹_____ like music. I can play the piano, but really ¹⁰_____ !

Let's ¹¹_____ over the Internet. Maybe I can be your exchange student – and then you can ¹²_____ England!

Let's speak ¹³_____ !

Best ¹⁴_____ ,

Libby McDonald

Mark: ____ /14

Total: ____ /24

1 Choose the correct answers (A–C) to complete the email.

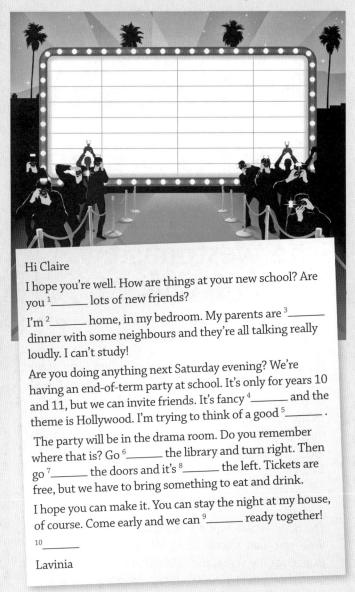

Hi Claire

I hope you're well. How are things at your new school? Are you ¹_____ lots of new friends?

I'm ²_____ home, in my bedroom. My parents are ³_____ dinner with some neighbours and they're all talking really loudly. I can't study!

Are you doing anything next Saturday evening? We're having an end-of-term party at school. It's only for years 10 and 11, but we can invite friends. It's fancy ⁴_____ and the theme is Hollywood. I'm trying to think of a good ⁵_____ .

The party will be in the drama room. Do you remember where that is? Go ⁶_____ the library and turn right. Then go ⁷_____ the doors and it's ⁸_____ the left. Tickets are free, but we have to bring something to eat and drink.

I hope you can make it. You can stay the night at my house, of course. Come early and we can ⁹_____ ready together!

¹⁰_____

Lavinia

1 A to make	B making	C make
2 A in	B on	C at
3 A doing	B going	C having
4 A clothes	B costume	C dress
5 A clothes	B costume	C dress
6 A past	B over	C on
7 A in	B about	C through
8 A on	B at	C in
9 A do	B go	C get
10 A Wishes	B Love	C Dear

Mark: ____ /10

2 Read the text about Libby's school. Find and correct one mistake in each line.

South London Academy is secondary school ¹_____

for students aged from 11 for 18. There ²_____

be about 800 students at the school and ³_____

42 members of staff. Students can to choose ⁴_____

from a big range of subjects, from economic ⁵_____

to ICT. Music and drama are a important part ⁶_____

of school life at the Academy. There isn't any ⁷_____

theatre for shows, but there's three music ⁸_____

rooms. And this year, we building a new ⁹_____

concert hall. Sport is important to: students ¹⁰_____

in years 1 to 4 are doing physical exercise ¹¹_____

every day. The Academy is the great place to ¹²_____

study. Students not have to pay because ¹³_____

it is a state school, and that is meaning that ¹⁴_____

education there is free.

Mark: ____ /14

Total: ____ /24

1 Choose the correct answers (A–D) to complete the postcard.

Dear Noah,

We're having a great ¹_____ in San Francisco.

On our first day, we rented bikes and ²_____ around the city for hours. We ³_____ the famous Golden Gate Bridge by bike. The view was amazing! By evening, we were really tired ⁴_____ there are lots of hills in San Francisco! ⁵_____ we visited Alcatraz, the famous prison on an island. It was really interesting.

We're going to a football match ⁶_____ evening. The 49ers ⁷_____ the Giants. I ⁸_____ know much about American Football, but it's exciting to watch. Tomorrow, we're ⁹_____ to Chinatown. We're flying home to the UK ¹⁰_____ Friday.

See you soon!

Tom

1 A fun	B holidays	C time	D days
2 A cycled	B walked	C visited	D explored
3 A arrived	B were	C cycled	D crossed
4 A because	B and	C but	D too
5 A Now	B Soon	C Tomorrow	D Yesterday
6 A this	B an	C in	D today
7 A play	B are playing	C played	D is playing
8 A am not	B don't	C can't	D have to
9 A visiting	B exploring	C arriving	D going
10 A in	B to	C on	D at

Mark: ____ /10

2 Choose the correct words to complete the text.

The Westminster Museum Café

The Westminster Museum is in the centre of London and the café is on the ¹**third** / **three** floor.

For a light lunch, try ²**any** / **some** delicious soup or a ³**sandwich** / **sandwiches**. You can choose from three different main meals every day. We prepare and cook all the food in our kitchens, so the dishes are always fresh and tasty. We don't use ⁴**any** / **some** processed food! There ⁵**are** / **is** always ⁶**any** / **some** vegetarian food on the menu.

Please note: we do not serve ⁷**an** / **any** alcoholic drinks.

The original café ⁸**open** / **opened** in 1971. At that time, you ⁹**can** / **could** order fish and chips for 50p! Over the years, the café served thousands of customers, but by 2000 it badly ¹⁰**needed** / **needs** repairs. So the café ¹¹**closed** / **closes** for nine months in 2001. During the repairs, they ¹²**add** / **added** an outdoor balcony with tables. The view is amazing – you can see the parks, concert ¹³**galleries** / **halls** and art ¹⁴**galleries** / **halls** of the city centre and the theatres of London's West End.

Mark: ____ /14

Total: ____ /24

1 Complete the text with the correct form of the words in brackets.

If you're a ¹_____ (visit) in Bangkok and you want a quiet meal in a small, family restaurant, the Royal Dragon is probably the ²_____ (bad) place you can go! According to *Guinness World Records*, it's the ³_____ (large) restaurant in the world. It employs about 1,000 members of staff and can serve food to 5,000 customers at the same time. It's a seafood restaurant, but it also serves ⁴_____ (tradition) Chinese, Japanese and Korean dishes, and some ⁵_____ (Europe) food too. Every evening, there is some form of ⁶_____ (entertain): Thai music, dance or ⁷_____ (box). And the waiters are also ⁸_____ (interest) to watch. They wear roller skates so they can bring the food to the tables ⁹_____ (quick). The staff in the kitchen have to work fast too. When they aren't ¹⁰_____ (cook) food for the customers, there are 25,000 plates to wash every day!

Mark: ____ /10

2 Choose the correct words to complete the letter.

Dear Anna,

How are you? I hope you're having a good time there in Poland. ¹**Was / Were** your parents happy to see you again? Did they ²**miss / missed** you? We miss you here in England!

I'm sending you the CD that I ³**tell / told** you about – the Noisettes. It's their first album – they ⁴**make / made** it in 2007. I think it's their ⁵**best / goodest** album. Their second album was ⁶**more / most** successful than their first, but that's only because one of the songs ⁷**was / were** in a TV advert! Anyway, I hope you like it.

My brother ⁸**gets / got** home yesterday from a two-week holiday in Peru. He ⁹**did go / went** with a group of friends to Machu Picchu in the mountains and ¹⁰**saw / see** the amazing buildings there. He took lots of great photos. I'm sending one with this letter.

Did Libby ¹¹**tell / told** you about our exam results? I ¹²**didn't / don't** pass maths, so I have to take it again next month. But Libby ¹³**didn't fail / failed** any exams. In fact, her results were the best ¹⁴**in / from** the class!

That's all for now. Write or email soon!

Best wishes,

George

Mark: ____ /14

Total: ____ /24

1 Complete the newspaper story with appropriate words.

Charity Ride

Two nurses from the north of England ¹_____ going to cycle from Land's End to John o' Groats to raise money for new hospital equipment. Joe Swain and Bella King are both nurses at Bradford Royal Infirmary ²_____ Yorkshire. The hospital badly needs a new running machine for the physiotherapy department, and Joe and Bella ³_____ decided to raise the money themselves.

John o' Groats in Scotland is the ⁴_____ north you can go on land in the UK. Land's End is on the southwest coast of England. Traditionally, the journey ⁵_____ these two places is the longest in the UK. By road, it is about 1,400 km.

So ⁶_____ long will it take Joe and Bella? 'We're hoping ⁷_____ do it in ten days,' says Joe. 'But perhaps we'll need two weeks.'

The two nurses have planned the journey very carefully. They are going to do it ⁸_____ May because the weather will be warm (they hope!) but not hot. At the moment, ⁹_____ training hard. 'We cycle every day,' says Bella. 'And ¹⁰_____ weekends, we do a long ride – 100 km or more. I'm getting very fit!'

Mark: ___ /10

2 Complete the formal letter with the words in the box.

application   be   going   jacket   just   receptionist
sincerely   to   uniform   will   won't   yet   you
you'll

Dear Ms Nowak,

Thank you for your ¹_____ to work at Golden Hills Holiday Camp. I am writing to confirm that we have offered you a job as a ²_____ . Congratulations!

We will provide a ³_____ – it is simply a red skirt and ⁴_____ and a white blouse. You ⁵_____ live in one of the special caravans for staff. The caravans are quite large and very comfortable, so I hope you will ⁶_____ happy there.

We've ⁷_____ offered work to five new employees, so you ⁸_____ be the only new person here. I'm ⁹_____ to organise a dinner for all the staff next month. I'm sure ¹⁰_____ make lots of friends here.

Please reply to this letter and confirm that ¹¹_____ accept the job. When are you going ¹²_____ arrive in England? Have you booked your flight ¹³_____ ? Let me know if you need any help. I look forward to working with you soon!

Yours ¹⁴_____ ,

Maggie Harrison

Mark: ___ /14

Total: ___ /24

Before reading

1 Look at the photos. Label the places with the words in the box.

| bookshop café market pub restaurant |

2 What can you do at each place in exercise 1? Complete the sentences.

1 People often go to a _____ for breakfast, a snack or just a drink.

2 At a _____ adults can meet friends, drink beer and sometimes have a meal too.

3 People go to a _____ for lunch or dinner, not just a drink or snack.

4 A _____ is often outside in the street, and you can buy lots of different things there.

5 You can buy books at a _____ .

While reading

3 Read the text. Underline the names of two hotels and three streets. Then circle the names of four areas in London that are mentioned.

4 Are these sentences true (T) or false (F)?

1 Covent Garden is a big shop in London. _____

2 There are lots of bookshops on Charing Cross Road. _____

3 You can buy clothes at Petticoat Lane and Old Spitalfields markets. _____

4 It's difficult to find good restaurants in Soho. _____

5 Afternoon tea at the Savoy Hotel is not expensive. _____

6 Food in London pubs is not usually very expensive. _____

Oxford Street has many big shops – Selfridges, Marks and Spencer, Debenhams. For smaller shops, go to Covent Garden. Charing Cross Road is famous for its bookshops. There are lots of them, and they sell old and new books.

At weekends you can visit some of London's markets. Petticoat Lane market (open on Sundays) is in Middlesex Street and has cheap clothes and things for the home. At the market in Portobello Road (open on Saturdays) you can buy old clocks, old chairs and tables, and hundreds of other things. At Brick Lane market (open on Sundays) in the East End, you can buy nearly everything. Old Spitalfields Market in Commercial Street (open on Sundays) has some of the latest clothes in town – and they're cheap!

When it is time for food, London has everything. You can have dinner in an expensive restaurant for hundreds of pounds – or you can buy a sandwich for not very much at all. You can eat in cafés or bars, you can buy food and take it away, and of course you can buy English fish and chips!

London has restaurants from nearly every country in the world and not all of them are expensive. You can find food from Italy, Mexico, Spain, India, China, Russia, and many other countries. There are hundreds of good restaurants in Picadilly, Soho, Leicester Square and Covent Garden, and more in Kensington, Knightsbridge and Chelsea.

For a very English afternoon, go to the Ritz in Picadilly or the Savoy Hotel in the Strand for afternoon tea. You can listen to music, drink tea and eat wonderful food. But remember to take a lot of money with you!

And do not forget about pubs. There are thousands of pubs in London. In many pubs, you can eat and drink, and pub food is often cheap and good.

After reading

5 INTERNET CHALLENGE Underline the names of four markets in the second paragraph of the text. Find them on an online map of London and say if they are in the east or west of the city.

6 Imagine a tourist is visiting your nearest town or city. Write five pieces of information about places to shop and eat.

The text is from Oxford Bookworms: 'London', by John Escott.

Before reading

1 Look at the pictures. Is the story about the past, the present or the future? Give two different reasons.

2 Using the pictures only, decide whether:

1 the man is rich or poor.

2 the girl is happy or sad.

3 the woman is friendly or unfriendly.

While reading

3 Read the text and find the names of the father, the daughter and the woman. Check your ideas from exercise 2.

One cold winter day a little girl and her father arrived in London. Sara Crewe was seven years old, and she had long black hair and green eyes. She sat in the cab next to her father and looked out of the window at the tall houses and the dark sky.

'What are you thinking about, Sara?' Mr Crewe asked. 'You are very quiet.' He put his arm round his daughter.

'I'm thinking about our house in India,' said Sara. 'And the hot sun and the blue sky. I don't think I like England very much, Father.'

'Yes, it's very different from India,' her father said. 'But you must go to school in London, and I must go back to India and work.'

'Yes, Father, I know,' said Sara. 'But I want to be with you. Please come to school with me! I can help with your lessons.'

Mr Crewe smiled, but he was not happy. He loved his little Sara very much, and he did not want to be without her. Sara's mother was dead, and Sara was his only child. Father and daughter were very good friends.

Soon they arrived at Miss Minchin's School for Girls and went into the big house.

Miss Minchin was a tall woman in a black dress. She looked at Sara, and then gave a very big smile.

'What a beautiful child!' she said to Mr Crewe.

4 Answer the questions.

1 What is the weather like when Sara and her father arrive in London?

2 Where were Sara and her father before London?

3 Why can't Sara and her father live in the same place?

4 Why does Miss Minchin call Sara 'a beautiful child'?

5 What nationality was Sara's mother?

6 Who is Amelia?

After reading

5 Complete the sentences with the words in the box to find out what happens in the rest of the story.

become invites is learns loses moves stays wants

1 Sara's father _____ all his money and dies in India.

2 Sara _____ at the school but becomes a servant.

3 Life for Sara _____ very hard but she is kind.

4 A man called Mr Carrisford _____ into the house next to the school with his Indian servant.

5 Mr Carrisford _____ to find the daughter of his dead friend, Ralph Crewe.

6 Sara and the Indian servant _____ friends.

7 By chance, Mr Carrisford _____ that Sara is Ralph Crewe's daughter.

8 Mr Carrisford _____ Sara to live with him. She is happy again – and rich.

6 **INTERNET CHALLENGE** Find out when the story was written. Find two more books by the same author.

Sara stood quietly and watched Miss Minchin. 'Why does she say that?' she thought. 'I am not beautiful, so why does she say it?'

Sara was not beautiful, but her father was rich. And Miss Minchin liked girls with rich fathers, because it was good for the school (and good for Miss Minchin, too).

'Sara is a good girl,' Mr Crewe said to Miss Minchin. 'Her mother was French, so she speaks French well. She loves books, and she reads all the time. But she must play with the other girls and make new friends, too.'

'Of course,' said Miss Minchin. She smiled again. 'Sara is going to be very happy here, Mr Crewe.'

Mr Crewe stayed in London for a week. He and Sara went to the shops, and he bought many beautiful, expensive dresses for his daughter. He bought books, and flowers for her room, and a big doll with beautiful dresses, too.

Miss Minchin smiled, but she said to her sister Amelia: 'All that money on dresses for a child of seven! She looks like a little princess, not a schoolgirl!'

The story is from Oxford Bookworms: 'A Little Princess', by Frances Hodgson Burnett.

Before reading

1 INTERNET CHALLENGE Choose the correct word in these sentences. Check online if necessary.

1 Antarctica is the **coldest / warmest** continent.

2 It's the **wettest / driest** continent.

3 It's the **windiest / sunniest** continent.

4 It's the furthest **south / north** of the continents.

5 It's **bigger / smaller** than Europe.

2 Look at the photo. In your opinion, what are the best and worst things about being in Antarctica? Use the adjectives in the box or your own ideas.

| beautiful cold dangerous empty exciting |

While reading

3 Read the text about Captain Scott, a British explorer, and his famous expedition to the South Pole. Answer the questions.

1 How many men in Scott's expedition reached the South Pole?

2 How many men died on the way home?

3 Where did the other group of Englishmen find Scott's body?

4 What happened on these dates in 1912?

1 16ᵗʰ February

2 9ᵗʰ March

3 17ᵗʰ March

4 26ᵗʰ October

After reading

5 Why do you think Captain Oates chose to die? Think of three possible reasons.

6 INTERNET CHALLENGE Find out about Roald Amundsen's expedition the same year. How was it different from Scott's?

Captain Scott and four other men reached the South Pole on 17ᵗʰ January 1912, but they didn't win the race – Amundsen and his men reached the Pole first. Tired and sad, Scott and his men started the difficult and dangerous journey home …

Scott's men were always hungry. There were not many depots and they were difficult to find. *We need to find the next depot today*, Oates wrote. *But how can we find one black flag, in all this snow? It's very difficult. And there is food for four men, not five.*

They were all tired and ill, too. Oates's feet were black now, and he could not feel them. On 16ᵗʰ February, Edgar Evans died.

On the 17ᵗʰ they were past the mountains. At the depot there they ate one of the dead ponies. Then they went on – ten, eleven, twelve kilometres a day. They were ill because their clothes were not warm and they didn't have much food. The temperature was sometimes -40°Centigrade.

On 7ᵗʰ March Scott looked at Oates's feet. They were big and black. 'I can't pull the sledge now,' Oates said. 'It's very difficult to walk. Am I going to lose these feet, Captain?'

Scott looked at Oates's feet, and said nothing.

On 9ᵗʰ March they found another depot, but there was not much food. Slowly, they walked on. Oates's feet were worse every day.

17ᵗʰ March was Oates's birthday. He was thirty-two. He lay in the tent and listened to the wind outside. He was very cold, very hungry, and very tired.

He wrote a letter to his mother and gave it to Wilson. Then he got up, and opened the door of the tent. He stopped in the door for a minute. Scott, Wilson, and Bowers looked at him. They didn't speak.

'I'm going outside for a minute,' Oates said. 'I may be some time.'

They didn't see him again.

* * * * *

At Cape Evans, another group of Englishmen waited. On 11ᵗʰ December, Meares and the dogs came back. On 3ʳᵈ January, Teddy Evans and his two men arrived at Cape Evans. The *Terra Nova* came, and went. Winter began. Scott did not come.

The Englishmen waited all winter at Cape Evans. Then, on 26ᵗʰ October 1912, they started for the south. Two weeks later, they found a tent.

There were three bodies in the tent – Scott, Wilson, and Bowers. They put the bodies under the snow. Then they took the men's letters and diaries, and went north to Cape Evans again.

In Scott's diary they read: *Oates died like a good Englishman. We all did. Please, remember us, and look after our families. We did our best.*

No one found Oates's body. But he is there, somewhere, under the snow and the wind, in the coldest, emptiest place on earth.

The text is from Oxford Bookworms: 'The Coldest Place on Earth', by Tim Vicary.

Before reading

1 What can you buy at a fast food restaurant? Make a list of food and drink.

2 Look at the picture. What are the customers doing? How do they feel?

While reading

3 Read the extract from a play called *Slow Food*. How many chefs work at the fast food restaurant?

4 Are these sentences true (T) or false (F)?

1 The customers are happy to wait for their food. _____

2 Maggie doesn't tell the truth at first. _____

3 Maggie enjoys her job. _____

4 The customers decide to change their lives and slow down. _____

5 Maggie serves the customers their food in the end. _____

6 Maggie leaves the restaurant before the customers. _____

After reading

5 Was Maggie right or wrong to leave her job suddenly? Give reasons for your opinion.

6 Work in a group. Practise reading the play, then film a performance to show the class.

Five Short Plays

People	We want our food!
Maggie	Please, everybody. Please! Your food is coming. He's doing it now.
People	*He?*
Maggie	Sorry, *they*. The chefs are doing it now.
Man 2	How many chefs have you got?
Maggie	Oh, lots.
Woman 2	How many?
Maggie	Some.
Woman 1	How many exactly? Tell us!
[...]	
Maggie	Well, er ... one.
People	One!
Maggie	No, sorry. That's wrong —
Man 1	I'm happy to hear it!
Maggie	We haven't got *any*.
People	What?
Maggie	That's right. There's only me here. Our last chef left yesterday. He was fed up with fast food.
Man 2	Fed up?
Maggie	Yes. He said to me, 'That's it! Enough! No more fast food for me! I'm going!' And he went.
Woman 2	But what about our —
Maggie	And do you know? I'm fed up too. Yes, I'm really, really fed up. Fast chicken, fast burgers, fast French fries, fast coke, fast coffee, fast talking, fast walking, fast eating, fast sleeping, fast living, fast dying. I'm fed up with it all!
Woman 1	But who is going to —
Maggie	What's the matter with everybody these days? Why is everything so fast? Come here. *(Maggie walks to the window.)* Come on! *(The people all go to the window.)* Look outside. Go on, look! It's a beautiful day. Life is beautiful. We can all be happy. But first we must slow down. We must take the time to *live*.
Man 1	Live? But we have to work!
Woman 3	We have lots to do.
Woman 1	And we want food.
Man 2	We want *fast* food —
Woman 1	Not *slow* food!
Woman 2	We haven't got time to —
Maggie	Time! Time! Time! Don't talk to me about time. You don't understand it. You – oh, it's no good, you're not listening to me.
She takes off her work clothes and picks up a bag.	
Woman 3	Hey, where are you going?
Maggie	I'm going out. I'm going to sit in the sun. I'm going to look at the sky and listen to the sea. I'm going to do nothing ... *slowly!*
Woman 1	But what about our food?
Man 2	What about my burger?
Maggie	*You* can do it.
Man 2	*What* did you say?
Maggie	I said, you can do it. Behind me is the kitchen. In the kitchen there's a big bag of chicken and another bag of burgers. You can do your own food, and you can do it as fast as you like. Goodbye!
People	But we don't —
Maggie	And have a nice day!
She goes out.	

The extract is from Oxford Bookworms: 'Five Short Plays', by Martyn Ford.

Before reading

1 INTERNET CHALLENGE **What do you know about the** *Titanic*? **Choose the correct answers. Check online if necessary.**

1 The *Titanic* made its first journey in _____ .

   a 1812   b 1912   c 1952

2 The *Titanic* was the _____ ship in the world at that time.

   a biggest   b fastest   c slowest

3 The *Titanic* sank in the _____ Ocean.

   a Pacific   b Indian   c Atlantic

4 The *Titanic* sank during its _____ journey.

   a first   b second   c third

2 **Describe the photo. What is happening? What are the people doing? How do they feel?**

While reading

3 **Read the text. Why did the** *Titanic* **sink? Choose the best reason.**

a The iceberg made holes in five compartments.

b The ship was going too fast when it hit the iceberg.

c The engines didn't work after the accident.

4 **Put the events in the correct order.**

1 The *Titanic* stops.

2 The *Titanic* hits an iceberg.

3 Thomas Andrews tells Mrs Astor, a passenger, that the *Titanic* cannot sink.

4 Murdoch tells the captain about the accident.

5 Smith, Murdoch and Andrews find water in five compartments.

6 Jack Phillips sends an emergency message.

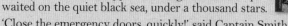

Captain Smith heard the noise too. He got out of bed quickly. 'What's wrong?' he asked First Officer Murdoch. 'What was that noise?'

'An iceberg, sir,' Murdoch answered. 'I'm very sorry, but we hit an iceberg. I'm stopping the engines.'

Slowly, the *Titanic* stopped. The big, beautiful ship waited on the quiet black sea, under a thousand stars.

'Close the emergency doors, quickly!' said Captain Smith.

'They are closed, sir.'

'That's good. Well done.'

When the fifteen emergency doors were closed, water could not move along the ship, from one compartment into the next one. But how many holes were there in the ship? Was there just one hole in one compartment, or were there a lot of holes, in a lot of compartments? Captain Smith wanted to know the answer – quickly.

Captain Smith, First Officer Murdoch, and Thomas Andrews, the designer of the *Titanic*, went down into the ship. They found a lot of holes. There was water in compartments 1, 2, 3, 4 and 5. 'How bad is this?' Captain Smith asked.

Thomas Andrews' face was white; he looked very unhappy. 'Very bad, I'm afraid,' he answered. 'This ship is going to sink.'

'What do you mean?' Captain Smith said. 'The *Titanic* can't sink. You said that to Mrs Astor yesterday! I heard you!'

'Yes, I know,' Andrews said. 'The *Titanic* is safe with water in three compartments. In fact, it is nearly safe with water in four compartments. But this – this is different. The water is coming into *five* compartments. *Five*. The front of the ship is going to get heavier and heavier – I'm sorry, but we can't stop it. The *Titanic* is going to sink.'

'How long have we got?' Captain Smith asked.

'I don't know. Two hours, perhaps. That's all.'

'Right. Give the passengers their life jackets, and get the lifeboats ready,' Smith said to Murdoch. Then he walked into the radio room to speak to the *Titanic*'s radio operator, Jack Phillips.

'This is an emergency,' Captain Smith said. 'The ship is sinking. Ask for help.'

'Yes, sir,' Jack Phillips answered. He sent the emergency message. 'CQD – MGY (Help – *Titanic*). We are sinking. Please come to help us.' It was 12.15 a.m.

After reading

5 INTERNET CHALLENGE *Titanic* **is also the name of a famous film about the disaster. Complete the information.**

Name of film: *Titanic*

Year: _____

Director: _____

Stars: _____

6 **Imagine you are Jack Phillips, the radio operator. Write a second message (20–30 words) an hour later. Explain what is happening now and ask for help again.**

The text is from Oxford Bookworms: 'Titanic', by Tim Vicary.

Functions Bank

MEETING PEOPLE

Good morning.

Good afternoon.

How are you?

Fine, thanks. And you?

Hi, I'm [Toby]. (1F)

Nice to meet you (too). (1F)

How old are you? (1F)

I'm [seventeen]. (1F)

This is [Annabel]. (1F)

Where are you from? (1F)

I'm from [Brighton]. (1F)

Have you got any brothers and sisters? (1F)

I've got [a brother] and [a sister]. (1F)

How old are they? (1F)

My brother is [14] and my sister is [18]. (1F)

GIVING AN OPINION

Do you like [video games]? (2F)

What's your favourite [video game]? (2F)

Are you interested in [fashion]? (2F)

They're OK. (2F)

She's all right. (2F)

They're terrible. (2F)

I can't stand him. (2F)

I love her. (2F)

I hate it. (2F)

He's awful. (2F)

I think she's great. (2F)

I'm not very keen on him. (2F)

They're boring. (2F)

I'm very keen on her. (2F)

It's brilliant. (2F)

I'm really into it. (2F)

I quite like them. (2F)

I really like her. (2F)

They're not bad. (2F)

I prefer [sports games]. (2F)

GIVING DIRECTIONS

Excuse me. Where's the [science lab]? (3F)

It's opposite [classroom 7]. (3F)

Go along this corridor. (3F)

Turn left/right. (3F)

Go through the doors. (3F)

Go down the stairs. (3F)

Go past the library. (3F)

It's on the left/right. (3F)

MAKING ARRANGEMENTS

What are you up to [this weekend]? (4F)

Are you doing anything [tonight]? (4F)

Are you free [in the afternoon]? (4F)

Let's [go shopping]. (4F)

How about [going for a bike ride]? (4F)

Yes, OK. What time? (4F)

Shall we meet at my house at [2 o'clock] on [Saturday afternoon]? (4F)

Fine. See you then! (4F)

That's perfect. (4F)

That sounds fun. (4F)

I'm afraid I can't. (4F)

IN A CAFÉ

Can I help you? (5F)

Yes, I'd like [the beef and mushroom pie], please. (5F)

Certainly. Here you are. (5F)

Anything to drink? (5F)

I'd like [a chocolate milkshake]. (5F)

And for you? (5F)

Are you paying together? (5F)

Yes, we are. (5F)

That's [£18], please. (5F)

Can I have the bill, please? (5F)

I'm sorry. We haven't got [tomato soup]. (5F)

Functions Bank

ASKING FOR INFORMATION

I'd like some information about [the gallery], please. (6F)

Certainly. What would you like to know? (6F)

What are your opening times? (6F)

What time do you open and close? (6F)

We open at [half past nine] and we close at [five o'clock]. (6F)

How much does it cost to get in? (6F)

How much are the tickets? (6F)

It's [$10] for adults and [$5] for children under 14. (6F)

Where is [the gallery] exactly? (6F)

Can you tell me where [the gallery] is? (6F)

You're welcome. (6F)

TALKING ABOUT YOUR WEEKEND

How was your weekend? (7F)

It was OK/good/terrible. (7F)

What did you do on [Saturday evening]? (7F)

What did you see? (7F)

I stayed in. / I watched [a really good film]. / I went on Facebook. / I went [to the cinema]. / I played [basketball]. (7F)

Cool! (7F)

Oh dear! (7F)

Oh no! (7F)

Poor you! (7F)

Really? (7F)

Sounds fun! (7F)

What a disaster! (7F)

What a shame! (7F)

Wow! (7F)

NEGOTIATING

Shall we [go on a skiing holiday]? (8F)

I don't think that's a good idea. (8F)

I don't like [skiing]. (8F)

How about [camping]? (8F)

Hmm, I don't know. (8F)

I'd prefer to [go on a city break]. / I'd rather [go on a city break]. (8F)

I think [going skiing] would be [nicer/better/more exciting]. (8F)

That sounds good. (8F)

Why don't we [go to Madrid] instead? (8F)

That's perfect. (8F)

ON THE PHONE

Good morning. Can I help you? (9F)

Yes, this is [Harry Jackson]. (9F)

I'd like to speak to [George Simpson]. (9F)

Can I speak to [George Simpson]? (9F)

I'm sorry. [Mr Simpson] isn't available at the moment. (9F)

Yes, speaking. (9F)

Can I take a message? (9F)

I'm afraid [Mr Simpson] isn't here. (9F)

I'm afraid [Mr Simpson] is on the phone. (9F)

Can I leave a message? (9F)

Can I give [Mr Simpson] a message? (9F)

Could you ask him to call me back, please? (9F)

Yes, of course. Has he got your number? (9F)

It's [01993 553725]. (9F)

And your name is? (9F)

What's your name? (9F)

Can he/she call me back, please? (9F)

I'll ask him to call you. (9F)

Thank you. Goodbye. (9F)

I'll call you back. (9F)

BUYING TRAIN TICKETS

Can I have a single/return ticket to [Oxford], please? (10F)

How much is a return ticket, with a railcard? (10F)

I'd like a ticket to [Bristol] please. (10F)

Single or return? (10F)

Return, please. (10F)

Are you coming back today? (10F)

When are you coming back? (10F)

Are you coming back on the same day? (10F)

Can I take my bike on the train? (10F)

That's [£15], please. (10F)

Which platform is it? (10F)

Which platform does it go from? (10F)

When's the next train? (10F)

The next train is at [13.45]. (10F)

Is it a direct train? (10F)

No, you have to change at [Swindon]. (10F)

Can I take my dog on the train? (10F)

Messages (personal profile)

- You can start the message with a greeting like *Hello!*, *Hi there!* or *Hi!* .
- Messages often start with basic personal information: name, age, school, home, family, etc.
- You do not need to use formal language in this kind of message.
- When you describe your hobbies and interests, give examples: When/Where do you do the activities? Which are your favourites?

> Hi there! My name is Maya and I'm sixteen years old. I'm in year 11 at West Hill Secondary School in Manchester. I live near the centre of Manchester with my mum, my two sisters and my stepdad. I haven't got any brothers.
> I love sport. I'm not really into football, but I usually play basketball or tennis at the weekend. I like music too. I play the guitar and I write songs. I sing too, but I'm not very good! My favourite singers are Adele and Beyoncé.

Announcements

> ## Drama Club
>
> Do you want to be on stage? Join the drama club and take part in our next show!
>
> We meet every Wednesday after school from 4 p.m. to 6 p.m. in the music room. Every term, we put on a different show in the school hall for students and teachers. We also make a video of the show and put it online. Visit our website and watch our old shows!
>
> For more details, email Connor: info@schooldramaclub.co.uk

- The first sentence should draw people's attention to the announcement. It shouldn't be too long. A question is a good way of doing this.
- Imperatives are often used in announcements.
- Put the contact details at the end.

Informal letters

- You can start the letter with *Dear* and the person's first name.
- You can start by asking how the person is.
- Divide the letter into short paragraphs, each with its own topic.
- You can end the letter with an expression like *Write soon*, *Best wishes*, or *Take care*, and your first name. If you know the person well, you can use *Love*, *Lots of love* or *With love from*.
- Use *PS* to add extra information or ask a question at the end of the letter.

> Dear Holly,
>
> How are you? Welcome to Green Hill Secondary School. I hope you enjoy your week with us. Here is some information about our school.
>
> Lessons start at 9.00 in the morning, but you have to be at school by 8.30 for assembly. Morning break is at 10.30. There are two lessons before the break and two after.
>
> Lunch is from 12.00 until 1.00. You can bring sandwiches or buy lunch in the canteen. The food is OK.
>
> There are usually three lessons in the afternoon, but on Wednesdays we do sport. You have to bring shorts, a T-shirt and trainers.
>
> I hope this information is helpful!
>
> Best wishes,
>
> Faith
>
> PS You have to switch off your mobile phone in lessons!

Writing Bank

Invitations

- You can start the invitation with *Dear* or *Hi* and the person's name.
- Abbreviations like *e.g.*, *etc.*, *St*, or *Rd* are often used.
- The text isn't usually divided into paragraphs.
- You can also add a phrase like *I hope you can make it* or *Hope you can come*.
- You can finish with *Love* or *Best wishes* and your name.

> Hi Alisha,
> We're having a Halloween party on Saturday 30ᵗʰ October from 8 p.m. until late. Please come! It's at the village hall in Back St. It's a fancy-dress party, so wear a costume. Can you invite your sisters too?
> Hope you can all make it.
> Love,
> Adam

Formal letters of application

> Dear Sir or Madam,
>
> I am writing to apply for a holiday job in your department store. I saw the advertisement on your website.
>
> I am eighteen years old and a full-time student at Worthington College. Last summer, I worked in a mobile phone shop, so I have experience of serving customers.
>
> I am very interested in this job because I want to get some work experience before I start university. I believe I am the right person for the job because I am hard-working and reliable.
>
> I am enclosing my CV and a reference from the manager of the mobile phone shop.
>
> I look forward to hearing from you.
>
> Yours faithfully,
> Dylan Jarvis

- Start the letter with *Dear* and the person's title and surname. Use *Mr* for men, *Ms* for women.
- If you don't the know the name of the person you are writing to, start the letter *Dear Sir or Madam*.
- Divide the letter into paragraphs, each with its own topic.
- In the first paragraph, say why you are writing.
- In the second paragraph, give some basic information about yourself and your experience.
- In the third paragraph, say why you want the job and why you are right for the job.
- In the final paragraph, say what you are enclosing with the letter.
- If you want a reply, you can write *I look forward to hearing from you* after the final paragraph.
- Do not use colloquial language or short forms, e.g. *I'm, you're*.
- Finish the letter with *Yours sincerely* if you used the person's name at the start, or *Yours faithfully* if you didn't. Write your whole name.

Postcards

- You can start a postcard with *Dear* or *Hi* and the person's first name.
- You can mention where you are staying, the weather, the people and the food.
- Mention some activities and/or plans.
- Use short forms, e.g. *We're* and *I'll*.
- You don't have to divide the text into paragraphs.
- Write short sentences, e.g. *The weather's awful. It rained all day yesterday.*
- Finish the postcard with a friendly phrase such as *Wish you were here, See you soon, Love* or *Bye for now!*.

> Dear Amelia,
> We're on holiday in Italy. We're staying in a nice hotel near the sea. The weather is OK – it isn't sunny at the moment, but it's warm and dry. The people here are very friendly and the food is great. We've had pasta every day! Yesterday, we visited a castle. It was really interesting. Tomorrow we're going on a boat trip. I haven't bought any souvenirs yet, but I hope we can find a good shop soon.
> Bye for now,
> Zoe

Wordlist

This list contains the key words from the units in the Student's Book.

Do you want more words, plus audio, definitions, context sentences and quizzes?
Go to www.oup.com/elt/solutions/wordsapp for the Solutions 2nd edition Words app.

Word	Phonetics	Translation
Introduction		
actress (n)	/'æktrəs/	*актриса*
basket (n)	/'bɑːskɪt/	*корзина*
bike (n)	/baɪk/	
date of birth (n)	/ˌdeɪt əv 'bɜːθ/	*дата рождения*
divided by (v)	/dɪ'vaɪdɪd ˌbaɪ/	
equal (v)	/'iːkwəl/	
favourite (adj)	/'feɪvərɪt/	*любимый*
first (det)	/fɜːst/	*первый*
half (n)	/hɑːf/	*половина*
independence day (n)	/ˌɪndɪ'pendəns deɪ/	
quarter (n)	/'kwɔːtə(r)/	*четверть*
second (det)	/'sekənd/	*второй*
skateboard (n)	/'skeɪtbɔːd/	*скейтборд*
third (det)	/θɜːd/	*третий*
thirsty (adj)	/'θɜːsti/	
trainers (n)	/'treɪnəz/	
times (prep)	/taɪmz/	
twelfth (det)	/twelfθ/	*двенадцатый*
twentieth (det)	/'twentiəθ/	*двадцатый*
Unit 1 Friends and family		
allow (v)	/ə'laʊ/	
alone (adv)	/ə'ləʊn/	
appearance (n)	/ə'pɪərəns/	
attractive (adj)	/ə'træktɪv/	
aunt (n)	/ɑːnt/	*тетя*
beard (n)	/bɪəd/	
bell (n)	/bel/	
charity (n)	/'tʃærəti/	
choose (v)	/tʃuːz/	
Christmas (n)	/'krɪsməs/	
come from (v)	/'kʌm frɒm, frəm/	
community (n)	/kə'mjuːnəti/	
competition (n)	/ˌkɒmpə'tɪʃn/	
couple (n)	/'kʌpl/	
cousin (n)	/'kʌzn/	
daughter (n)	/'dɔːtə(r)/	
decision (n)	/dɪ'sɪʒn/	
different (adj)	/'dɪfrənt/	
dinner (n)	/'dɪnə(r)/	
dish (n)	/dɪʃ/	
dress (n)	/dres/	
dress (v)	/dres/	
duchess (n)	/'dʌtʃəs/	
duty (n)	/'djuːti/	
eldest (adj)	/'eldɪst/	
election (n)	/ɪ'lekʃn/	
enjoy (v)	/ɪn'dʒɔɪ/	
event (n)	/ɪ'vent/	
exciting (adj)	/ɪk'saɪtɪŋ/	
fly (v)	/flaɪ/	
free time (n)	/ˌfriː 'taɪm/	
get up (phr v)	/ˌget 'ʌp/	
government (n)	/'gʌvənmənt/	
granddaughter (n)	/'grændɔːtə(r)/	
grandparent (n)	/'grænpeərənt/	
great-grandparent (n)	/ˌgreɪt 'grænpeərənt/	
grow up (phr v)	/ˌgrəʊ 'ʌp/	
hate (v)	/heɪt/	
homework (n)	/'həʊmwɜːk/	
housework (n)	/'haʊswɜːk/	
husband (n)	/'hʌzbənd/	
interviewer (n)	/'ɪntəvjuːə(r)/	
king (n)	/kɪŋ/	

Word	Phonetics	Translation
law (n)	/'lɔː/	
leader (n)	/'liːdə(r)/	
local (adj)	/'ləʊkl/	
married (adj)	/'mærid/	
match (n)	/mætʃ/	
maths (n)	/mæθs/	
mean (v)	/miːn/	
member (n)	/'membə(r)/	
mention (v)	/'menʃn/	
miss (v)	/mɪs/	
modern (adj)	/'mɒdn/	
moustache (n)	/mə'stɑːʃ/	
neighbour (n)	/'neɪbə(r)/	
nephew (n)	/'nefjuː/	
niece (n)	/niːs/	
noisy (adj)	/'nɔɪzi/	
occasion (n)	/ə'keɪʒn/	
official (adj)	/ə'fɪʃl/	
old-fashioned (adj)	/ˌəʊld 'fæʃnd/	
ordinary (adj)	/'ɔːdnri/	
originally (adv)	/ə'rɪdʒənəli/	
parent (n)	/'peərənt/	
people (n)	/'piːpl/	
pet (n)	/pet/	
potato (n)	/pə'teɪtəʊ/	
pop (adj)	/pɒp/	
power (n)	/'paʊə(r)/	
practise (v)	/'præktɪs/	
prepare (v)	/prɪ'peə(r)/	
prince (n)	/prɪns/	
queen (n)	/kwiːn/	
quiet (adj)	/'kwaɪət/	
reason (n)	/'riːzn/	
royal (adj)	/'rɔɪəl/	
sandwich (n)	/'sænwɪtʃ/	
scary (adj)	/'skeəri/	
simple (adj)	/'sɪmpl/	
skiing (n)	/'skiːɪŋ/	
son (n)	/sʌn/	
stepbrother (n)	/'stepbrʌðə(r)/	
stepdad (n)	/'stepdæd/	
suit (n)	/suːt/	
support (v)	/sə'pɔːt/	
talent show (n)	/'tælənt ʃəʊ/	
tourism (n)	/'tʊərɪzəm/	
twin (n)	/twɪn/	
uncle (n)	/'ʌŋkl/	
unusual (adj)	/ʌn'juːʒuəl/	
usually (adv)	/'juːʒuəli/	
volleyball (n)	/'vɒlibɔːl/	
vote (v)	/vəʊt/	
what (det)	/wɒt/	
when (adv)	/wen/	
where (adv)	/weə(r)/	
which (det)	/wɪtʃ/	
who (pro)	/huː/	
whose (pro)	/huːz/	
wife (n)	/waɪf/	
word (n)	/wɜːd/	

Get Ready for your Exam 1

Word	Phonetics	Translation
community (n)	/kə'mjuːnəti/	
old-fashioned (adj)	/ˌəʊld'fæʃnd/	
relative (n)	/'relətɪv/	
school exchange (n)	/ˌskuːl ɪks'tʃeɪndʒ/	

Wordlist

Word	Phonetics	Translation
step-brother (n)	/'stepbrʌðə/	----------------
surfing (n)	/'sɜːfɪŋ/	----------------

Unit 2 My time

Word	Phonetics	Translation
accident (n)	/'æksɪdənt/	----------------
activity (n)	/æk'tɪvəti/	----------------
amazing (adj)	/ə'meɪzɪŋ/	----------------
athletics (n)	/æθ'letɪks/	----------------
awful (adj)	/'ɔːfl/	----------------
back (n)	/bæk/	----------------
ballroom dancing (n)	/ˌbɔːlruːm 'dɑːnsɪŋ/	----------------
band (n)	/bænd/	----------------
bat (n)	/bæt/	----------------
beautifully (adv)	/'bjuːtɪfli/	----------------
beat (v)	/biːt/	----------------
beginner (n)	/bɪ'gɪnə(r)/	----------------
board game (n)	/'bɔːd geɪm/	----------------
bowling (n)	/'bəʊlɪŋ/	----------------
bridge (n)	/brɪdʒ/	----------------
building (n)	/'bɪldɪŋ/	----------------
can't stand (v)	/ˌkɑːnt 'stænd/	----------------
carefully (adv)	/'keəfəli/	----------------
cave diving (n)	/'keɪv daɪvɪŋ/	----------------
cheer (v)	/tʃɪə(r)/	----------------
cheerleading (n)	/'tʃɪəliːdɪŋ/	----------------
chess (n)	/tʃes/	----------------
chest (n)	/tʃest/	----------------
climb (v)	/klaɪm/	----------------
compete (v)	/kəm'piːt/	----------------
crowd (n)	/kraʊd/	----------------
cycling (n)	/'saɪklɪŋ/	----------------
dancing (n)	/'dɑːnsɪŋ/	----------------
dangerous (adj)	/'deɪndʒərəs/	----------------
darts (n)	/dɑːts/	----------------
deep (adj)	/diːp/	----------------
dive (v)	/daɪv/	----------------
diving (n)	/'daɪvɪŋ/	----------------
drama (n)	/'drɑːmə/	----------------
draw (v)	/drɔː/	----------------
drawing (n)	/'drɔːɪŋ/	----------------
entertain (v)	/ˌentə'teɪn/	----------------
especially (adv)	/ɪ'speʃəli/	----------------
extremely (adv)	/ɪk'striːmli/	----------------
fashion (n)	/'fæʃn/	----------------
finger (n)	/'fɪŋgə(r)/	----------------
fit (adj)	/fɪt/	----------------
fluently (adv)	/'fluːəntli/	----------------
forget (v)	/fə'get/	----------------
free running (n)	/ˌfriː 'rʌnɪŋ/	----------------
front (n)	/frʌnt/	----------------
get out (phr v)	/ˌget 'aʊt/	----------------
ground (n)	/graʊnd/	----------------
happen (v)	/'hæpən/	----------------
hardly ever (adv)	/ˌhɑːdli 'evə(r)/	----------------
healthy (adj)	/'helθi/	----------------
helmet (n)	/'helmɪt/	----------------
hill (n)	/hɪl/	----------------
hit (v)	/hɪt/	----------------
ice hockey (n)	/'aɪs hɒki/	----------------
ice skating (n)	/'aɪs skeɪtɪŋ/	----------------
interested (adj)	/'ɪntrəstɪd/	----------------
join (v)	/dʒɔɪn/	----------------
jump (v)	/dʒʌmp/	----------------
keen on (adj)	/'kiːn ɒn/	----------------
keeping fit (n)	/ˌkiːpɪŋ 'fɪt/	----------------

Word	Phonetics	Translation
letter (n)	/'letə(r)/	----------------
lie down (phr v)	/ˌlaɪ 'daʊn/	----------------
light (n)	/laɪt/	----------------
loud (adj)	/laʊd/	----------------
midnight (n)	/'mɪdnaɪt/	----------------
neck (n)	/nek/	----------------
often (adv)	/'ɒfn, 'ɒftən/	----------------
parachute (n)	/'pærəʃuːt/	----------------
post (v)	/pəʊst/	----------------
prefer (v)	/prɪ'fɜː(r)/	----------------
pretty (adj)	/'prɪti/	----------------
prize (n)	/praɪz/	----------------
quite (adv)	/kwaɪt/	----------------
race (n)	/reɪs/	----------------
reality (n)	/ri'æləti/	----------------
remember (v)	/rɪ'membə(r)/	----------------
reply (v)	/rɪ'plaɪ/	----------------
rollerblading (n)	/'rəʊləbleɪdɪŋ/	----------------
roof (n)	/ruːf/	----------------
routine (n)	/ruː'tiːn/	----------------
rule (n)	/ruːl/	----------------
score (v)	/skɔː(r)/	----------------
score (n)	/skɔː(r)/	----------------
sea (n)	/siː/	----------------
secondary school (n)	/'sekəndri skuːl/	----------------
shoulder (n)	/'ʃəʊldə(r)/	----------------
stupid (adj)	/'stjuːpɪd/	----------------
skilful (adj)	/'skɪlfl/	----------------
sometimes (adv)	/'sʌmtaɪmz/	----------------
sporty (adj)	/'spɔːti/	----------------
strong (adj)	/strɒŋ/	----------------
surfing the Net (n)	/ˌsɜːfɪŋ ðə 'net/	----------------
teenager (n)	/'tiːneɪdʒə(r)/	----------------
terrible (adj)	/'terəbl/	----------------
text message (n)	/'tekst mesɪdʒ/	----------------
tidy (v)	/'taɪdi/	----------------
tired (adj)	/'taɪəd/	----------------
toe (n)	/təʊ/	----------------
tomorrow (n)	/tə'mɒrəʊ/	----------------
turn off (phr v)	/ˌtɜːn 'ɒf/	----------------
type (v)	/taɪp/	----------------
uniform (n)	/'juːnɪfɔːm/	----------------
untidy (adj)	/ʌn'taɪdi/	----------------
view (n)	/vjuː/	----------------
wash up (phr v)	/ˌwɒʃ 'ʌp/	----------------
weather (n)	/'weðə(r)/	----------------
whistle (v)	/'wɪsl/	----------------
writer (n)	/'raɪtə(r)/	----------------
youth club (n)	/'juːθ klʌb/	----------------

Unit 3 At school

Word	Phonetics	Translation
angry (adj)	/'æŋgri/	----------------
arrive (v)	/ə'raɪv/	----------------
art and design (n)	/ˌɑːt ən dɪ'zaɪn/	----------------
assembly (n)	/ə'sembli/	----------------
athletics track (n)	/æθ'letɪks træk/	----------------
balance (n)	/'bæləns/	----------------
behind (prep)	/bɪ'haɪnd/	----------------
between (prep)	/bɪ'twiːn/	----------------
bin (n)	/bɪn/	----------------
blackboard (n)	/'blækbɔːd/	----------------
blind (n)	/blaɪnd/	----------------
board (n)	/bɔːd/	----------------
bored (adj)	/bɔːd/	----------------
break (n)	/breɪk/	----------------

Wordlist

Word	Phonetics	Translation
canteen (n)	/kænˈtiːn/	....
champion (n)	/ˈtʃæmpiən/	....
chest of drawers (n)	/ˌtʃest əv ˈdrɔːz/	....
concert hall (n)	/ˈkɒnsət hɔːl/	....
corridor (n)	/ˈkɒrɪdɔː(r)/	....
cupboard (n)	/ˈkʌbəd/	....
curtain (n)	/ˈkɜːtn/	....
design and technology (n)	/dɪˌzaɪn ən tekˈnɒlədʒi/	....
desk (n)	/desk/	....
dining room (n)	/ˈdaɪnɪŋ ruːm/	....
entrance (n)	/ˈentrəns/	....
facility (n)	/fəˈsɪləti/	....
famous (adj)	/ˈfeɪməs/	....
fencing (n)	/ˈfensɪŋ/	....
guide (n)	/gaɪd/	....
gym (n)	/dʒɪm/	....
hall (n)	/hɔːl/	....
headteacher's office (n)	/hedˈtiːtʃəz ɒfɪs/	....
heavy (adj)	/ˈhevi/	....
ICT (information and communication technology) (n)	/ˌaɪ siː ˈtiː, ɪnfəˌmeɪʃn ən kəmjuːnɪˌkeɪʃn tekˈnɒlədʒi/	
in front of (prep)	/ɪn ˈfrʌnt əv/	....
interview (n)	/ˈɪntəvjuː/	....
least (adj)	/liːst/	....
lose (v)	/luːz/	....
meal (n)	/miːl/	....
meat (n)	/miːt/	....
mistake (n)	/mɪˈsteɪk/	....
mixed (adj)	/mɪkst/	....
move (v)	/muːv/	....
near (prep)	/nɪə(r)/	....
next to (prep)	/ˈneks tə/	....
noticeboard (n)	/ˈnəʊtɪsbɔːd/	....
opposite (prep)	/ˈɒpəzɪt/	....
P.E. kit (n)	/ˌpiː ˈiː kɪt/	....
packed lunch (n)	/ˌpækt ˈlʌntʃ/	....
pay (v)	/peɪ/	....
pencil (n)	/ˈpensl/	....
physics (n)	/ˈfɪzɪks/	....
plant (n)	/plɑːnt/	....
playing field (n)	/ˈpleɪɪŋ fiːld/	....
poster (n)	/ˈpəʊstə(r)/	....
private (adj)	/ˈpraɪvət/	....
proud (adj)	/praʊd/	....
R.E. (religious education) (n)	/rɪˌlɪdʒəs edʒuˈkeɪʃn/	....
rowing (n)	/ˈrəʊɪŋ/	....
rubber (n)	/ˈrʌbə(r)/	....
ruler (n)	/ˈruːlə(r)/	....
science lab (n)	/ˈsaɪəns læb/	....
shower (n)	/ˈʃaʊə(r)/	....
snack (n)	/snæk/	....
state school (n)	/ˈsteɪt skuːl/	....
subject (n)	/ˈsʌbdʒɪkt/	....
swimming pool (n)	/ˈswɪmɪŋ puːl/	....
tennis court (n)	/ˈtenɪs kɔːt/	....
term (n)	/tɜːm/	....
textbook (n)	/ˈtekstbʊk/	....
toilet (n)	/ˈtɔɪlət/	....
touch (v)	/tʌtʃ/	....
upstairs (adv)	/ʌpˈsteəz/	....
wardrobe (n)	/ˈwɔːdrəʊb/	....
weigh (v)	/weɪ/	....

Word	Phonetics	Translation
wrestler (n)	/ˈreslə(r)/	....

Get Ready for your Exam 2

Word	Phonetics	Translation
boarding school (n)	/ˈbɔːdɪŋ skuːl/	....
boat (n)	/bəʊt/	....
brain (n)	/breɪn/	....
building (n)	/ˈbɪldɪŋ/	....
canteen (n)	/kænˈtiːn/	....
choir (n)	/ˈkwaɪə/	....
competition (n)	/ˌkɒmpəˈtɪʃn/	....
dangerous (adj)	/ˈdeɪndʒərəs/	....
fence (n)	/fens/	....
helmet (n)	/ˈhelmɪt/	....
hockey (n)	/ˈhɒki/	....
horseshoe (n)	/ˈhɔːsʃuː/	....
iron (adj)	/ˈaɪən/	....
island (n)	/ˈaɪlənd/	....
meal (n)	/miːl/	....
muscles (n)	/ˈmʌslz/	....
obstacle course (n)	/ˈɒbstəkl kɔːs/	....
packed lunch (n)	/ˌpækt ˈlʌntʃ/	....
primary school (n)	/ˈpraɪməri skuːl/	....
score (v)	/skɔː/	....
secondary school (n)	/ˈsekəndri skuːl/	....
stick (n)	/stɪk/	....
weigh (v)	/weɪ/	....

Unit 4 Special occasions

Word	Phonetics	Translation
according to (prep)	/əˈkɔːdɪŋ tə/	....
afraid (adj)	/əˈfreɪd/	....
barbecue (n)	/ˈbɑːbɪkjuː/	....
believe (v)	/bɪˈliːv/	....
bury (v)	/ˈberi/	....
candle (n)	/ˈkændl/	....
can't make it (v)	/ˌkɑːnt ˈmeɪk ɪt/	....
cardigan (n)	/ˈkɑːdɪgən/	....
celebrate (v)	/ˈselɪbreɪt/	....
costume (n)	/ˈkɒstjuːm/	....
curly (adj)	/ˈkɜːli/	....
decorate (v)	/ˈdekəreɪt/	....
dress (n)	/dres/	....
evil (adj)	/ˈiːvl/	....
fair (adj)	/feə(r)/	....
fancy dress (n)	/ˌfænsi ˈdres/	....
foreground (n)	/ˈfɔːgraʊnd/	....
ghost (n)	/gəʊst/	....
glove (n)	/glʌv/	....
good-looking (adj)	/ˌgʊd ˈlʊkɪŋ/	....
gothic (adj)	/ˈgɒθɪk/	....
graveyard (n)	/ˈgreɪvjɑːd/	....
groom (n)	/gruːm/	....
guest (n)	/gest/	....
Halloween (n)	/ˈhæləʊiːn/	....
harvest (v,n)	/ˈhɑːvɪst/	....
horror (adj)	/ˈhɒrə(r)/	....
invitation (n)	/ˌɪnvɪˈteɪʃn/	....
invite (v)	/ɪnˈvaɪt/	....
jacket (n)	/ˈdʒækɪt/	....
jeans (n)	/dʒiːnz/	....
joggers (n)	/ˈdʒɒgəz/	....
lantern (n)	/ˈlæntən/	....
matter (v)	/ˈmætə(r)/	....
outdoors (adv)	/aʊtˈdɔːz/	....
perfect (adj)	/ˈpɜːfɪkt/	....
relative (n)	/ˈrelətɪv/	....
request (n)	/rɪˈkwest/	....

Wordlist

Word	Phonetics	Translation
roller coaster (n)	/'rəʊlə kəʊstə(r)/	------------------
romantic (adj)	/rəʊ'mæntɪk/	------------------
sausage (n)	/'sɒsɪdʒ/	------------------
scarf (n)	/skɑːf/	------------------
secret (n)	/'siːkrət/	------------------
shall (v)	/ʃæl, ʃəl/	------------------
shine (v)	/ʃaɪn/	------------------
shirt (n)	/ʃɜːt/	------------------
shorts (n)	/ʃɔːts/	------------------
skirt (n)	/skɜːt/	------------------
smile (v)	/smaɪl/	------------------
sock (n)	/sɒk/	------------------
sound (v)	/saʊnd/	------------------
space (n)	/speɪs/	------------------
spirit (n)	/'spɪrɪt/	------------------
spring (n)	/sprɪŋ/	------------------
stand (v)	/stænd/	------------------
strange (adj)	/streɪndʒ/	------------------
sweets (n)	/swiːts/	------------------
theme (n)	/θiːm/	------------------
thin (adj)	/θɪn/	------------------
tie (n)	/taɪ/	------------------
topic (n)	/'tɒpɪk/	------------------
tracksuit (n)	/'træksuːt/	------------------
traditional (adj)	/trə'dɪʃənl/	------------------
trick or treating (n)	/ˌtrɪk ɔː 'triːtɪŋ/	------------------
trip (n)	/trɪp/	------------------
trousers (n)	/'traʊzəz/	------------------
venue (n)	/'venjuː/	------------------
wavy (adj)	/'weɪvi/	------------------
wedding (n)	/'wedɪŋ/	------------------
wish (n)	/wɪʃ/	------------------
witch (n)	/wɪtʃ/	------------------

Unit 5 Healthy living

Word	Phonetics	Translation
advice (n)	/əd'vaɪs/	------------------
baked (adj)	/beɪkt/	------------------
beef (n)	/biːf/	------------------
biscuit (n)	/'bɪskɪt/	------------------
boiled (adj)	/bɔɪld/	------------------
butter (n)	/'bʌtə(r)/	------------------
cabbage (n)	/'kæbɪdʒ/	------------------
carrot (n)	/'kærət/	------------------
cheese (n)	/tʃiːz/	------------------
chicken (n)	/'tʃɪkɪn/	------------------
chip (n)	/tʃɪp/	------------------
cure (v)	/kjʊə(r)/	------------------
customer (n)	/'kʌstəmə(r)/	------------------
dairy (adj)	/'deəri/	------------------
environment (n)	/ɪn'vaɪrənmənt/	------------------
fattening (adj)	/'fætnɪŋ/	------------------
fizzy (adj)	/'fɪzi/	------------------
fridge (n)	/frɪdʒ/	------------------
fried (adj)	/fraɪd/	------------------
fruit (n)	/fruːt/	------------------
garlic (n)	/'gɑːlɪk/	------------------
grape (n)	/greɪp/	------------------
ham (n)	/hæm/	------------------
health spa (n)	/'helθ spɑː/	------------------
honey (n)	/'hʌni/	------------------
ill (adj)	/ɪl/	------------------
juice (n)	/dʒuːs/	------------------
kind (n)	/kaɪnd/	------------------
lamb (n)	/læm/	------------------
laugh (v)	/lɑːf/	------------------

Word	Phonetics	Translation
leisure centre (n)	/'leʒə sentə(r)/	------------------
lifestyle (n)	/'laɪfstaɪl/	------------------
massage (n)	/'mæsɑːʒ/	------------------
medicine (n)	/'medsn/	------------------
milkshake (n)	/'mɪlkʃeɪk/	------------------
mushroom (n)	/'mʌʃrʊm, -ruːm/	------------------
noodle (n)	/'nuːdl/	------------------
nut (n)	/nʌt/	------------------
olive (n)	/'ɒlɪv/	------------------
onion (n)	/'ʌnjən/	------------------
painful (adj)	/'peɪnfl/	------------------
pea (n)	/piː/	------------------
pepper (n)	/'pepə(r)/	------------------
pie (n)	/paɪ/	------------------
pocket (n)	/'pɒkɪt/	------------------
pork (n)	/pɔːk/	------------------
prawn (n)	/prɔːn/	------------------
processed food (n)	/'prəʊsest ˌfuːd/	------------------
produce (v)	/prə'djuːs/	------------------
quantity (n)	/'kwɒntəti/	------------------
recipe (n)	/'resəpi/	------------------
roast (v)	/rəʊst/	------------------
salmon (n)	/'sæmən/	------------------
salt (n)	/sɔːlt, sɒlt/	------------------
seafood (n)	/'siːfuːd/	------------------
seed (n)	/siːd/	------------------
serve (v)	/sɜːv/	------------------
shellfish (n)	/'ʃelfɪʃ/	------------------
skin (n)	/skɪn/	------------------
snake (n)	/sneɪk/	------------------
soup (n)	/suːp/	------------------
stand up (phr v)	/ˌstænd 'ʌp/	------------------
stir fry (n)	/'stɜː fraɪ/	------------------
sun cream (n)	/'sʌn kriːm/	------------------
sweet (adj)	/swiːt/	------------------
take off (phr v)	/ˌteɪk 'ɒf/	------------------
take-away (n)	/'teɪk əweɪ/	------------------
tasty (adj)	/'teɪsti/	------------------
toasted (adj)	/'təʊstɪd/	------------------
treatment (n)	/'triːtmənt/	------------------
tuna (n)	/'tjuːnə/	------------------
unhealthy (adj)	/ʌn'helθi/	------------------
waste (n)	/weɪst/	------------------

Get Ready for your Exam 3

Word	Phonetics	Translation
allergy (n)	/'ælədʒi/	------------------
arrangements (n)	/ə'reɪndʒmənts/	------------------
background (n)	/'bækgraʊnd/	------------------
balloon (n)	/bə'luːn/	------------------
bush (n)	/bʊʃ/	------------------
candle (n)	/'kændl/	------------------
charity (n)	/'tʃærəti/	------------------
coin (n)	/kɔɪn/	------------------
dairy food (n)	/'deəri fuːd/	------------------
delicious (adj)	/dɪ'lɪʃəs/	------------------
diary (n)	/'daɪəri/	------------------
fair (n)	/feə(r)/	------------------
foreground (n)	/'fɔːgraʊnd/	------------------
noodles (n)	/'nuːdlz/	------------------
outfit (n)	/'aʊtfɪt/	------------------
rainforest (n)	/'reɪnfɒrɪst/	------------------
silly (adj)	/'sɪli/	------------------
vegan (n)	/'viːgən/	------------------
vegetarian (adj)	/ˌvedʒə'teəriən/	------------------
wig (n)	/wɪg/	------------------

Wordlist

Word	Phonetics	Translation

Unit 6 Going places

Word	Phonetics	Translation
achievement (n)	/əˈtʃiːvmənt/	-------------------
allowed (adj)	/əˈlaʊd/	-------------------
art gallery (n)	/ˈɑːt gæləri/	-------------------
birthday (n)	/ˈbɜːθdeɪ/	-------------------
bookshop (n)	/ˈbʊkʃɒp/	-------------------
borrow (v)	/ˈbɒrəʊ/	-------------------
broken (adj)	/ˈbrəʊkən/	-------------------
bus stop (n)	/ˈbʌs stɒp/	-------------------
catch (v)	/kætʃ/	-------------------
cheap (adj)	/tʃiːp/	-------------------
church (n)	/tʃɜːtʃ/	-------------------
cinema (n)	/ˈsɪnəmə/	-------------------
close (adj)	/kləʊs/	-------------------
close (v)	/kləʊz/	-------------------
congratulations (n)	/kənˌgrætʃuˈleɪʃnz/	-------------------
cycle (v)	/ˈsaɪkl/	-------------------
decide (v)	/dɪˈsaɪd/	-------------------
dent (n)	/dent/	-------------------
designer (n)	/dɪˈzaɪnə(r)/	-------------------
detailed (adj)	/ˈdiːteɪld/	-------------------
direction (n)	/dəˈrekʃn, dɪ-, daɪ-/	-------------------
entry (n)	/ˈentri/	-------------------
exhibition (n)	/ˌeksɪˈbɪʃn/	-------------------
experience (n)	/ɪkˈspɪəriəns/	-------------------
explain (v)	/ɪkˈspleɪn/	-------------------
fantastic (adj)	/fænˈtæstɪk/	-------------------
garage (n)	/ˈgærɑːʒ/	-------------------
gift voucher (n)	/ˈgɪft vaʊtʃə(r)/	-------------------
go straight on (v)	/gəʊ ˈstreɪt ˌɒn/	-------------------
grade (n)	/greɪd/	-------------------
harbour (n)	/ˈhɑːbə(r)/	-------------------
hurry (v)	/ˈhʌri/	-------------------
jewellery (n)	/ˈdʒuːəlri/	-------------------
modern art (n)	/ˌmɒdn ˈɑːt/	-------------------
national (adj)	/ˈnæʃnəl/	-------------------
nervous (adj)	/ˈnɜːvəs/	-------------------
notice (v)	/ˈnəʊtɪs/	-------------------
order (v)	/ˈɔːdə(r)/	-------------------
paint (v)	/peɪnt/	-------------------
parrot (n)	/ˈpærət/	-------------------
play (v)	/pleɪ/	-------------------
police station (n)	/pəˈliːs steɪʃn/	-------------------
post office (n)	/ˈpəʊst ɒfɪs/	-------------------
repair (v)	/rɪˈpeə(r)/	-------------------
shame (n)	/ʃeɪm/	-------------------
shark (n)	/ʃɑːk/	-------------------
shout (v)	/ʃaʊt/	-------------------
spend (v)	/spend/	-------------------
stamp (n)	/stæmp/	-------------------
surprised (adj)	/səˈpraɪzd/	-------------------
sympathy (n)	/ˈsɪmpəθi/	-------------------
ticket (n)	/ˈtɪkɪt/	-------------------
tournament (n)	/ˈtʊənəmənt/	-------------------
town hall (n)	/ˌtaʊn ˈhɔːl/	-------------------
urgent (adj)	/ˈɜːdʒənt/	-------------------
wallet (n)	/ˈwɒlɪt/	-------------------
wet (adj)	/wet/	-------------------
whisper (v)	/ˈwɪspə(r)/	-------------------
worry (v)	/ˈwʌri/	-------------------

Unit 7 Fame!

Word	Phonetics	Translation
annoying (adj)	/əˈnɔɪɪŋ/	-------------------
apologise (v)	/əˈpɒlədʒaɪz/	-------------------

Word	Phonetics	Translation
appear (v)	/əˈpɪə(r)/	-------------------
battle (n)	/ˈbætl/	-------------------
be born (v)	/ˌbi ˈbɔːn/	-------------------
border (n)	/ˈbɔːdə(r)/	-------------------
brave (adj)	/breɪv/	-------------------
build (v)	/bɪld/	-------------------
century (n)	/ˈsentʃəri/	-------------------
childhood (n)	/ˈtʃaɪldhʊd/	-------------------
cut off (phr v)	/ˌkʌt ˈɒf/	-------------------
deaf (adj)	/def/	-------------------
death (n)	/deθ/	-------------------
depressed (adj)	/dɪˈprest/	-------------------
disaster (n)	/dɪˈzɑːstə(r)/	-------------------
discover (v)	/dɪˈskʌvə(r)/	-------------------
dream (n)	/driːm/	-------------------
earth (n)	/ɜːθ/	-------------------
equal (adj)	/ˈiːkwəl/	-------------------
finally (adv)	/ˈfaɪnəli/	-------------------
forever (adv)	/fərˈevə(r)/	-------------------
galaxy (n)	/ˈgæləksi/	-------------------
get off (phr v)	/ˌget ˈɒf/	-------------------
get on (phr v)	/ˌget ˈɒn/	-------------------
gig (n)	/gɪg/	-------------------
gravity (n)	/ˈgrævəti/	-------------------
grow (v)	/grəʊ/	-------------------
hide (v)	/haɪd/	-------------------
honest (adj)	/ˈɒnɪst/	-------------------
illness (n)	/ˈɪlnəs/	-------------------
invent (v)	/ɪnˈvent/	-------------------
light bulb (n)	/ˈlaɪt bʌlb/	-------------------
look after (phr v)	/ˈlʊk ˌɑːftə(r)/	-------------------
machine (n)	/məˈʃiːn/	-------------------
mental illness (n)	/ˌmentl ˈɪlnəs/	-------------------
musician (n)	/mjuˈzɪʃn/	-------------------
nurse (n)	/nɜːs/	-------------------
pass (v)	/pɑːs/	-------------------
politely (adv)	/pəˈlaɪtli/	-------------------
prison (n)	/ˈprɪzn/	-------------------
record (v)	/rɪˈkɔːd/	-------------------
retire (v)	/rɪˈtaɪə(r)/	-------------------
right (n)	/raɪt/	-------------------
scientist (n)	/ˈsaɪəntɪst/	-------------------
section (n)	/ˈsekʃn/	-------------------
separate (adj)	/ˈseprət/	-------------------
seriously (adv)	/ˈsɪəriəsli/	-------------------
shoot (v)	/ʃuːt/	-------------------
show (v)	/ʃəʊ/	-------------------
social-networking site (n)	/ˌsəʊʃl ˈnetwɜːkɪŋ saɪt/	-------------------
speech (n)	/spiːtʃ/	-------------------
state (n)	/steɪt/	-------------------
sunlight (n)	/ˈsʌnlaɪt/	-------------------
take care (phr v)	/ˌteɪk ˈkeə(r)/	-------------------
take place (v)	/ˌteɪk ˈpleɪs/	-------------------
theology (n)	/θiˈɒlədʒi/	-------------------
war (n)	/wɔː(r)/	-------------------

Get Ready for your Exam 4

Word	Phonetics	Translation
armchair (n)	/ɑːmˈtʃeə(r)/	-------------------
bull fight (n)	/bʊl faɪt/	-------------------
calculator (n)	/ˈkælkjuleɪtə(r)/	-------------------
doorbell (n)	/ˈdɔːbel/	-------------------
fireplace (n)	/ˈfaɪəpleɪs/	-------------------
get married (v)	/get ˈmærid/	-------------------
invent (v)	/ɪnˈvent/	-------------------
knock (v)	/nɒk/	-------------------

Wordlist

Word	Phonetics	Translation
medal (n)	/ˈmedl/	-----------------
novel (n)	/ˈnɒvl/	-----------------
portrait (n)	/ˈpɔːtreɪt/	-----------------
prison (n)	/ˈprɪzn/	-----------------
rucksack (n)	/ˈrʌksæk/	-----------------
scratch (v)	/skrætʃ/	-----------------
shocked (adj)	/ʃɒkt/	-----------------
soldier (n)	/ˈsəʊldʒə(r)/	-----------------
staircase (n)	/ˈsteəkeɪs/	-----------------
statue (n)	/ˈstætʃuː/	-----------------
suddenly (adv)	/ˈsʌdənli/	-----------------
world record (n)	/wɜːld ˈrekɔːd/	-----------------

Unit 8 In the wild

Word	Phonetics	Translation
advertisement (n)	/ədˈvɜːtɪsmənt/	-----------------
average (n)	/ˈævərɪdʒ/	-----------------
base (n)	/beɪs/	-----------------
beak (n)	/biːk/	-----------------
bear (n)	/beə(r)/	-----------------
bird-watching (n)	/ˈbɜːd wɒtʃɪŋ/	-----------------
camping (n)	/ˈkæmpɪŋ/	-----------------
canoeing (n)	/kəˈnuːɪŋ/	-----------------
cardboard (n)	/ˈkɑːdbɔːd/	-----------------
cave (n)	/keɪv/	-----------------
ceiling (n)	/ˈsiːlɪŋ/	-----------------
climbing (n)	/ˈklaɪmɪŋ/	-----------------
creature (n)	/ˈkriːtʃə(r)/	-----------------
danger (n)	/ˈdeɪndʒə(r)/	-----------------
desert (n)	/ˈdezət/	-----------------
destroy (v)	/dɪˈstrɔɪ/	-----------------
die out (phr v)	/ˌdaɪ ˈaʊt/	-----------------
disappear (v)	/ˌdɪsəˈpɪə(r)/	-----------------
disease (n)	/dɪˈziːz/	-----------------
dolphin (n)	/ˈdɒlfɪn/	-----------------
eagle (n)	/ˈiːgl/	-----------------
east (n)	/iːst/	-----------------
elephant (n)	/ˈelɪfənt/	-----------------
exist (v)	/ɪgˈzɪst/	-----------------
explorer (n)	/ɪkˈsplɔːrə(r)/	-----------------
fierce (adj)	/fɪəs/	-----------------
fishing (n)	/ˈfɪʃɪŋ/	-----------------
flight (n)	/flaɪt/	-----------------
forest (n)	/ˈfɒrɪst/	-----------------
fossil (n)	/ˈfɒsl/	-----------------
habitat (n)	/ˈhæbɪtæt/	-----------------
hunt (v)	/hʌnt/	-----------------
inhabitant (n)	/ɪnˈhæbɪtənt/	-----------------
instead (adv)	/ɪnˈsted/	-----------------
island (n)	/ˈaɪlənd/	-----------------
kick (v)	/kɪk/	-----------------
killer whale (n)	/ˈkɪlə ˌweɪl/	-----------------
lake (n)	/leɪk/	-----------------
landmark (n)	/ˈlændmɑːk/	-----------------
lion (n)	/ˈlaɪən/	-----------------
measurement (n)	/ˈmeʒəmənt/	-----------------
mosquito (n)	/məˈskiːtəʊ/	-----------------
mountain biking (n)	/ˈmaʊntən ˌbaɪkɪŋ/	-----------------
necessary (adj)	/ˈnesəsəri/	-----------------
north (n)	/nɔːθ/	-----------------
objection (n)	/əbˈdʒekʃn/	-----------------
passenger (n)	/ˈpæsɪndʒə(r)/	-----------------
polar bear (n)	/ˌpəʊlə ˈbeə(r)/	-----------------
pollution (n)	/pəˈluːʃn/	-----------------
population (n)	/ˌpɒpjuˈleɪʃn/	-----------------
protect (v)	/prəˈtekt/	-----------------

Word	Phonetics	Translation
raise (v)	/reɪz/	-----------------
reptile (n)	/ˈreptaɪl/	-----------------
request (n,v)	/rɪˈkwest/	-----------------
rhino (n)	/ˈraɪnəʊ/	-----------------
sailing (n)	/ˈseɪlɪŋ/	-----------------
salty (adj)	/ˈsɔːlti, ˈsɒlti/	-----------------
scenery (n)	/ˈsiːnəri/	-----------------
size (n)	/saɪz/	-----------------
solar system (n)	/ˈsəʊlə sɪstəm/	-----------------
south (n)	/saʊθ/	-----------------
surface (n)	/ˈsɜːfɪs/	-----------------
talented (adj)	/ˈtæləntɪd/	-----------------
terror (n)	/ˈterə(r)/	-----------------
ugly (adj)	/ˈʌgli/	-----------------
valley (n)	/ˈvæli/	-----------------
volcano (n)	/vɒlˈkeɪnəʊ/	-----------------
waterfall (n)	/ˈwɔːtəfɔːl/	-----------------
west (n)	/west/	-----------------
wide (adj)	/waɪd/	-----------------
wild (adj)	/waɪld/	-----------------

Unit 9 The world of work

Word	Phonetics	Translation
ability (n)	/əˈbɪləti/	-----------------
aim (n)	/eɪm/	-----------------
application (n)	/ˌæplɪˈkeɪʃn/	-----------------
apply (v)	/əˈplaɪ/	-----------------
available (adj)	/əˈveɪləbl/	-----------------
boss (n)	/bɒs/	-----------------
builder (n)	/ˈbɪldə(r)/	-----------------
career (n)	/kəˈrɪə(r)/	-----------------
coach (n)	/kəʊtʃ/	-----------------
conservation (n, adj)	/ˌkɒnsəˈveɪʃn/	-----------------
CV	/ˌsiː ˈviː/	-----------------
deal with (v)	/ˈdiːl wɪð/	-----------------
degree (n)	/dɪˈgriː/	-----------------
director (n)	/dəˈrektə(r), dɪ-, daɪ-/	-----------------
earn (v)	/ɜːn/	-----------------
employ (v)	/ɪmˈplɔɪ/	-----------------
engineer (n)	/ˌendʒɪˈnɪə(r)/	-----------------
faithfully (adv)	/ˈfeɪθfəli/	-----------------
fix (v)	/fɪks/	-----------------
full-time (adj)	/ˈfʊl taɪm/	-----------------
gap year (n)	/ˈgæp jɪə(r)/	-----------------
hairdresser (n)	/ˈheədresə(r)/	-----------------
hard-working (adj)	/ˌhɑːd ˈwɜːkɪŋ/	-----------------
in charge of (adj)	/ɪn ˈtʃɑːdʒ əv/	-----------------
industry (n)	/ˈɪndəstri/	-----------------
journalist (n)	/ˈdʒɜːnəlɪst/	-----------------
lawyer (n)	/ˈlɔːjə(r)/	-----------------
lead (v)	/liːd/	-----------------
lifeguard (n)	/ˈlaɪfgɑːd/	-----------------
look forward (phr v)	/ˌlʊk ˈfɔːwəd/	-----------------
look up (phr v)	/ˌlʊk ˈʌp/	-----------------
madam (n)	/ˈmædəm/	-----------------
mechanic (n)	/məˈkænɪk/	-----------------
offer (v)	/ˈɒfə(r)/	-----------------
part-time (adj)	/ˈpɑːt taɪm/	-----------------
phrase (n)	/freɪz/	-----------------
plumber (n)	/ˈplʌmə(r)/	-----------------
poem (n)	/ˈpəʊɪm/	-----------------
polite (adj)	/pəˈlaɪt/	-----------------
provide (v)	/prəˈvaɪd/	-----------------
public (n)	/ˈpʌblɪk/	-----------------
qualification (n)	/ˌkwɒlɪfɪˈkeɪʃn/	-----------------
quality (n)	/ˈkwɒləti/	-----------------

Wordlist

Word	Phonetics	Translation
recent (adj)	/'ri:snt/	----------------------
reliable (adj)	/rɪ'laɪəbl/	----------------------
responsible (adj)	/rɪ'spɒnsəbl/	----------------------
sailor (n)	/'seɪlə(r)/	----------------------
save money (v)	/ˌseɪv 'mʌni/	----------------------
secretary (n)	/'sekrətri/	----------------------
shop assistant (n)	/'ʃɒp əsɪstənt/	----------------------
signature (n)	/'sɪgnətʃə(r)/	----------------------
sink (n)	/sɪŋk/	----------------------
ski instructor (n)	/'ski: ɪnstrʌktə(r)/	----------------------
software (n)	/'sɒftweə(r)/	----------------------
soldier (n)	/'səʊldʒə(r)/	----------------------
stable (n)	/'steɪbl/	----------------------
success (n)	/sək'ses/	----------------------
take a year off (v)	/ˌteɪk ə ˌjɪər 'ɒf/	----------------------
therapist (n)	/'θerəpɪst/	----------------------
useful (adj)	/'ju:sfl/	----------------------
usher (n)	/'ʌʃə(r)/	----------------------
vacancy (n)	/'veɪkənsi/	----------------------
vet (n)	/vet/	----------------------
voluntary (adj)	/'vɒləntri/	----------------------
volunteer (n)	/ˌvɒlən'tɪə(r)/	----------------------

Get Ready for your Exam 5

Word	Phonetics	Translation
avoid (v)	/ə'vɔɪd/	----------------------
bills (n)	/bɪlz/	----------------------
bite (n)	/baɪt/	----------------------
career (n)	/kə'rɪə(r)/	----------------------
drinking water (n)	/'drɪŋkɪŋ 'wɔ:tə(r)/	----------------------
earn (v)	/ɜ:n/	----------------------
fighter jet (n)	/'faɪtə(r) dʒet/	----------------------
first-aid kit (n)	/ˌfɜ:st'eɪd kɪt/	----------------------
hero (n)	/'hɪərəʊ/	----------------------
immunisation (n)	/ˌɪmjunaɪ'zeɪʃn/	----------------------
insect repellent (n)	/'ɪnsekt rɪ'pelənt/	----------------------
mosquito (n)	/mɒski:təʊ/	----------------------
peel (v)	/pi:l/	----------------------
rent (v)	/rent/	----------------------
sickness (n)	/'sɪknəs/	----------------------
sleeve (n)	/sli:v/	----------------------
soft drink (n)	/ˌsɒft 'drɪŋk/	----------------------
spider (n)	/'spaɪdə(r)/	----------------------
stomach ache (n)	/'stʌmək eɪk/	----------------------
sun cream (n)	/sʌn kri:m/	----------------------
surgery (n)	/'sɜ:dʒəri/	----------------------
theme park (n)	/'θi:m pɑ:k/	----------------------

Unit 10 Time to travel

Word	Phonetics	Translation
accommodation (n)	/əˌkɒmə'deɪʃn/	----------------------
already (adv)	/ɔ:l'redi/	----------------------
ancestor (n)	/'ænsestə(r)/	----------------------
announcement (n)	/ə'naʊnsmənt/	----------------------
artificial (adj)	/ˌɑ:tɪ'fɪʃl/	----------------------
break down (phr v)	/ˌbreɪk 'daʊn/	----------------------
convenient (adj)	/kən'vi:niənt/	----------------------
crash into (v)	/ˌkræʃ 'ɪntə/	----------------------
descendant (n)	/dɪ'sendənt/	----------------------
destination (n)	/ˌdestɪ'neɪʃn/	----------------------
direct (adj)	/də'rekt, dɪ-, daɪ-/	----------------------
district (n)	/'dɪstrɪkt/	----------------------
enormous (adj)	/ɪ'nɔ:məs/	----------------------
experienced (adj)	/ɪk'spɪəriənst/	----------------------
explore (v)	/ɪk'splɔ:(r)/	----------------------
fall off (v)	/ˌfɔ:l 'ɒf/	----------------------
gap (n)	/gæp/	----------------------

Word	Phonetics	Translation
get back (phr v)	/ˌget 'bæk/	----------------------
get in (phr v)	/ˌget 'ɪn/	----------------------
give someone a lift (v)	/ˌgɪv ... ə 'lɪft/	----------------------
go on foot (v)	/ˌgəʊ ɒn 'fʊt/	----------------------
hike (v)	/haɪk/	----------------------
inconvenient (adj)	/ˌɪnkən'vi:niənt/	----------------------
iron (v)	/'aɪən/	----------------------
label (n)	/'leɪbl/	----------------------
luggage (n)	/'lʌgɪdʒ/	----------------------
market (n)	/'mɑ:kɪt/	----------------------
narrow (adj)	/'nærəʊ/	----------------------
nowadays (adv)	/'naʊədeɪz/	----------------------
pack (v)	/pæk/	----------------------
patiently (adv)	/'peɪʃntli/	----------------------
permission (n)	/pə'mɪʃn/	----------------------
postcard (n)	/'pəʊstkɑ:d/	----------------------
queue (n)	/kju:/	----------------------
railcard (n)	/'reɪlkɑ:d/	----------------------
realise (v)	/'ri:əlaɪz/	----------------------
recently (adv)	/'ri:sntli/	----------------------
refuse (v)	/rɪ'fju:z/	----------------------
rescue (v)	/'reskju:/	----------------------
rope (n)	/rəʊp/	----------------------
single (adj)	/'sɪŋgl/	----------------------
successful (adj)	/sək'sesfl/	----------------------
suitcase (n)	/'su:tkeɪs/	----------------------
take off (phr v) [plane]	/ˌteɪk 'ɒf/	----------------------
tiring (adj)	/'taɪərɪŋ/	----------------------
trapped (adj)	/træpt/	----------------------
underground train (n)	/'ʌndəgraʊnd ˌtreɪn/	----------------------
yet (adv)	/jet/	----------------------
youth hostel (n)	/'ju:θ hɒstl/	----------------------

Self Check answers

Unit 1

1
1 uncle
2 cousin
3 grandfather
4 nephew
5 niece
6 grandchildren
7 grandparents
8 aunt

2
1 universities
2 buses
3 women
4 photos
5 children
6 shelves

3
1 get up
2 watches
3 speak
4 like
5 has

4
1 My parents don't get up early on Sundays.
2 Anna doesn't watch TV in her bedroom.
3 My brother and I don't speak five languages.
4 You don't like tomatoes.
5 My sister doesn't have swimming lessons.

5
1 Does Anna play tennis? Yes, she does.
2 Do your cousins live near here? No, they don't.
3 Does your dad speak French? No, he doesn't.
4 Do Mike and Andy have music lessons? Yes, they do.
5 Do you and your friends go out a lot? No, we don't.
6 Do you like sport? Yes, I/we do.

Unit 2

1
1 skateboarding
2 board games
3 ice hockey
4 athletics
5 jogging
6 fashion
7 rollerblading
8 gymnastics

2
1 does
2 play
3 go
4 chat
5 play
6 watches

3
1 Mark sometimes gets up before seven.
2 He usually goes to work by bus.
3 He's never late for work.
4 He hardly ever has lunch at home.
5 He always watches TV in the evening.
6 He's usually in bed before midnight.

4
1 Can Jason swim? No, he can't.
2 Can you use a computer? Yes, I can.
3 Can Tom and Anna drive? Yes, they can.
4 Can Mary speak French? No, she can't.

5
1 beautifully
2 hard
3 well
4 badly
5 easily
6 late

Unit 3

1
1 maths
2 art and design
3 chemistry
4 ICT
5 history
6 P.E.

2
1 kitchen ✓
2 chest of drawers
3 stairs ✓
4 living room ✓
5 wardrobe
6 notice board

3
2 There is a clock in my bedroom.
3 There aren't any shelves in the bathroom.
4 There are some cupboards in the dining room.
5 There isn't a study in the house.
6 There aren't any curtains in the living room.

4
1 Is there a … ? Yes, there is.
2 Are there any … ? No, there aren't.
3 Are there any … ? Yes, there are.

5
1 behind
2 between
3 under
4 in front of

6
1 Do … have to; don't
2 have to
3 don't have to
4 doesn't have to
5 Does … have to; does
6 doesn't have to

Unit 4

1
1 socks
2 jacket
3 boots
4 shirt
5 trousers
6 scarf
7 trainers
8 gloves

2
1 tall
2 glasses
3 moustache
4 dark
5 curly
6 fair

3
1 is having
2 aren't watching
3 is chatting
4 are playing
5 isn't dancing
6 aren't making

4
1 Who are we meeting
2 What are you having
3 Where are we playing
4 Why is he wearing

5
1 are … doing
2 'm playing
3 Do … want
4 don't like
5 's shining
6 'm winning

Unit 5

1
1 chicken
2 eggs
3 potato
4 butter
5 salmon
6 peas
7 rice

2
1 baked
2 grilled
3 fried
4 roasted

3
1 tuna
2 pork
3 beef
4 butter

4
1 How many
2 How many
3 How much
4 How much
5 How many

5
1 should work
2 should ask
3 shouldn't use
4 shouldn't ride
5 should read
6 shouldn't eat

6
1 When should she send
2 How should I cook
3 Where should we put
4 What should they wear

Unit 6

1

1 post office
2 concert hall
3 bus stop
4 art gallery
5 library

2

1 order
2 leave
3 night club
4 park

3

1 d
2 c
3 a
4 b

4

1 was
2 Were ... weren't
3 wasn't
4 were

5

1 couldn't play
2 could walk
3 couldn't go
4 couldn't sleep

6

1 stayed
2 watched
3 listened
4 phoned
5 chatted
6 tidied

7

1 the day before yesterday
2 three months ago
3 last week

Unit 7

1

1 American
2 Turkey
3 Japanese
4 Brazil
5 French
6 the Republic of Ireland
7 Swedish
8 the Czech Republic

2

1 have
2 make
3 do
4 have
5 take

3

1 slept
2 sold
3 wrote
4 won
5 spent
6 bought

4

1 didn't arrive
2 didn't wear
3 didn't go
4 didn't send
5 didn't begin
6 didn't visit

5

1 What did Ann do
2 Did Mark play
3 When did Mark do
4 Did Ann play
5 When did Ann do

Unit 8

1

1 cave ... waterfall
2 river ... forest
3 island ... lake
4 mountain ... beach
5 volcano ... sea

2

1 Europe
2 South America
3 Asia
4 Africa

3

1 How tall is your uncle?
2 The beach is two kilometres away.
3 The swimming pool is two metres deep.
4 How heavy is an African elephant?

4

1 Martha is taller than Jack.
2 Porsches are more expensive than Skodas.
3 Skiing is safer than climbing.
4 I think Greek food is worse than Italian food.
5 Polar bears are bigger than lions.

5

1 highest
2 deepest
3 longest
4 furthest
5 most popular
6 safest
7 hottest

Unit 9

1

1 electrician
2 waiter
3 scientist
4 engineer
5 builder
6 hairdresser
7 soldier
8 architect

2

1 sail**or**
2 guitar**ist**
3 direct**or**
4 mana**ger**

3

1 I'm not going to be at school tomorrow.
2 You aren't going **to** study this weekend.
3 My mum and dad **are** going to stay at home.
4 We **aren't** going to have a holiday this year.

4

1 Are Mason and his family going to have a holiday next month? Yes, they are.
2 Is Mason going to send any postcards? No, he isn't.
3 Is his dad going to take his laptop? Yes, he is.
4 Are Mason and his brother going to share a room? No, they aren't.

5

1 won't need
2 will earn
3 won't be
4 will finish
5 'll enjoy

6

1 will you be
2 Will you be
3 I won't
4 Will you walk
5 I will

Unit 10

1

1 scooter
2 helicopter
3 van
4 lorry
5 tram
6 underground train

2

1 c
2 a
3 d
4 b

3

1 down
2 out of
3 down
4 off
5 out

4

1 's just started
2 've just bought
3 's just left
4 's just arrived
5 's just finished

5

1 hasn't tidied his bedroom yet.
2 He's already done his homework.
3 He hasn't helped with the cooking yet.
4 He's already practised the guitar.
5 He hasn't phoned Max yet.

6

1 Has ... packed; she has
2 Have ... found; they haven't
3 Have ... bought; I have
4 Has ... written; he hasn't
5 Have ... changed; we have